Suppressed History

Suppressed History

Obliterating Politically Correct Orthodoxies

B. Forrest Clayton

Second Edition

Armistead Publishing - Cincinnati, Ohio

Suppressed History
Obliterating Politically Correct Orthodoxies
B. Forrest Clayton

Published by:
Armistead Publishing
P.O. Box 54516
Cincinnati, OH 45254

ISBN, print ed. 0-9723920-0-9
First Printing 2003
Printed in the United States of America

Suppressed History - 3

Contents

About the Author
Acknowledgements

1	Introduction	7
2	Custer at Gettysburg	21
3	Crockett's Death at the Alamo	31
4	Women In Combat	61
5	The Optimistic Environmentalist	81
6	Einstein v. Bohr on Quantum Physics	92
7	The Sphinx and Geology	103
8	Darwinian Evolution	113
9	Kennewick Man	136
10	Conclusion	151

Bibliography

About the Author

B. Forrest Clayton is a graduate of Northern Kentucky University where he received a Bachelors degree in History. He is also a graduate of Xavier University where he received a Masters degree in Education. He taught U.S. History and World History for seven years, before becoming a free-lance writer. He was motivated to write this book when he realized that key historical facts, events, and people were being omitted from the textbooks as well as the nightly news broadcasts.

Acknowledgments

To my father who initially sparked within me a passion for the study of history.

I would like to acknowledge those that specifically granted me permission to reproduce copyrighted material: Cambridge University Press (excerpts from Bjorn Lomborg's book *The Skeptical Environmentalist* were reprinted with the permission of Cambridge University Press), Robert K. Brown (founder of *Soldier of Fortune*), Carver Mead-*Collective Electrodynamics* and the MIT Press, Old Army Press, and *American Spectator*. I would also like to thank those who wrote the copyright law provision known as the fair use doctrine. Finally, I would like to thank the Founding Fathers; in particular, for writing the First Amendment, and in general for writing the Declaration of Independence and the U.S. Constitution, which made possible the formation of the greatest, freest country in the history of the world. May God continue to bless the United States of America.

"There is nothing new in the world except the history you do not know."

Harry S. Truman

1
Introduction

"...The truth shall make you free."
-Jesus Christ

"And ye shall know the truth, and the truth shall make you free" (John 8:32). The goal of education in the past was to seek out the truth and to disseminate knowledge. The goal of education today is to promote a post-modernist version of diversity, multiculturalism, and political correctness, in spite of the truth. So-called educators want to disseminate self-esteem and social skills, not knowledge. The educational establishment and the "mainstream" news media consider many pieces of factual knowledge to be dirty little secrets that should be kept from the masses at all costs. These facts do not fit within the politically correct paradigm, and therefore these facts are omitted from the curriculum and the airwaves. The goal of this book is to uncover suppressed history, to bring forth important facts that have been omitted from the curriculum and to seek out the truth wherever it may lead.

The general public does not know about the information contained in this book. The information is out there, but it is not publicized. It is not widely known. Many history and political science professors with PhDs do not even know about the information contained in this book. I recently asked a professor with a PhD in history if he had ever heard of "Kennewick Man." He replied, "No, I am not familiar with him. Who is he?" That was the crystallizing moment when I decided to write this book and make an attempt to publicize it to the people who would like to know, but have been let down by the textbooks and the "mainstream media."

This book is an attempt, in modern business jargon, to "think outside the box." This book is an attempt to publicize researchers and their evidence, which does not appear in the textbooks and on the nightly news broadcasts. This book is an attempt to "connect the dots" which have yet to be fully connected. As Plato preached, "All knowledge is interrelated." Specialization and fragmentation have their place, but the specialist must guard against seeing only one tree in great detail, and missing the forest. This book is an attempt to see the whole forest.

Thomas Kuhn in his book *The Structure of Scientific Revolutions* explains how scientists operate on the basis of an assumed paradigm. The scientists and academics for the most part hold to this orthodoxy, and all their subsequent observations are viewed only through the prism of this paradigm. When the scientists find pieces of evidence that do not fit within the assumed paradigm, those pieces of evidence are labeled as anomalous and are swept under the rug. They are ignored. The textbooks and the media suppress the information. This is especially true if the threatened paradigm has political ramifications. Zealots support certain "scientific" orthodoxies dogmatically, because they know that if their particular "scientific" paradigm/theory collapses it would inevitably destroy their philosophical and political worldview. It would crush their souls. It would reveal that the distinguished emperor has no clothes. They believe it must be prevented at all costs. They believe it must be prevented even if it requires suppressing evidence and destroying the livelihoods of honest whistleblowers who dare to point out the truth- the truth that the particular paradigm is flawed and therefore must be changed to reflect the newly found evidence.

Cremo and Thompson in their book *Forbidden Archeology* call this suppression of evidence in academic circles a "knowledge filter." Anomalous evidence is ignored. Cremo and Thompson were featured on the documentary "The Mysterious Origins of Man," hosted by Charlton Heston. This video pointed out the fact that Virginia Steen-McIntyre, an honest professional geologist, in 1966 discovered tools and spear points in Hueyatlaco, Mexico that dated 250,000 years old. She used radio metric dates, uranium atoms, and Zircon crystals. This evidence was anomalous. It went against the existing paradigm of when humans supposedly first settled the "New World". She reported her results. It ruined her career. She was blacklisted. She could never again find employment in her own profession. This is why many honest scientists are scared to speak out against the orthodox paradigm. It could destroy their careers.

Another example of this phenomenon is Bernard Goldberg, formerly of CBS News. Bernard Goldberg used to work with Dan Rather and was on good terms with the hierarchy of CBS News. Bernard Goldberg says that he is a traditional liberal Democrat. But the key point is that he is an honest man who is willing to speak out and reveal the truth about what is going on in the "mainstream" news media.

Mr. Goldberg wrote an op-ed piece in the *Wall Street Journal*, which revealed evidence of a left wing liberal bias at CBS News. He also wrote a book entitled *Bias -- A CBS Insider Exposes How The Media Distort The News*. It was published by Regnery in 2002 and became a bestseller. Bernard Goldberg believes that Dan Rather kept him from becoming a correspondent on 60 Minutes II in retaliation for his op-ed piece about liberal bias in the media. CBS News did not renew Mr. Goldberg's contract after he wrote his op-ed piece. CBS News seems to have blacklisted Bernard Goldberg because they wouldn't even cover his nation-wide best selling book. They felt the need to suppress.

The courageous journalist John Leo of *U.S. News & World Report* pointed out many examples of suppressed history. On June 10, 1996, his "On Society" column was entitled "All the News that Fits Our Biases". His title was adapted from Herman H. Dinsmore's book *All the News that Fits*, which was a scathing attack on the *New York Times* for its left wing liberal bias, by the former editor of the international edition of the *New York Times*. It was roughly the equivalent of Bernard Goldberg's book *Bias*. Dinsmore and Leo were poking fun at the *New York Times* mantra "All the News That's Fit To Print."

Mr. Leo points out that when "Democratic Senator Daniel Patrick Moynihan of New York told *New York Post* reporter Deborah Orin he would vote to override President Clinton's veto of the partial-birth abortion ban bill because partial birth abortions are 'too close to infanticide,'" the following newspapers suppressed the story: the *Washington Post*, the *L.A. Times*, the *Boston Globe*, and the *New York Times*. They ignored it. They acted as if it never happened. Left wing physicists who follow in Neils Bohr's footsteps would say they did the right thing. Because according to them, Schrodinger's cat is neither alive nor dead until someone opens the box to observe it. They believe that if we don't observe or read about partial birth abortions, then they must not exist. They think that the baby, like the cat, is neither alive nor dead; it is merely in a state of quantum limbo. According to left wing academics, there is no objective reality. They claim that Neils Bohr proved this. But Einstein, Carver Mead, and George Gilder know that the left wing Bohrian paradigm is false. As maverick physicist Carver Mead, the inventor of the Foveon camera says, "Bohr's complementarity is crap." (*Forbes*, March 18, 2002, page No. 39.)

John Leo put it best in his *U.S. News* column on May 20th, 2002. Why should the left wing controlled news media or academia debate the facts when they have the power to suppress the facts and prevent any debate at all? Leo asks, "Why debate when you can suppress?" Leo states that on our college campuses "normal intellectual give-and-take have largely disappeared. Free speech, open debate, and full disclosure" are being destroyed by the left wing academics that control our college campuses. "Why [should they] debate when [they] can suppress?"

Georgetown University in Washington D.C. no longer requires English literature majors to study Shakespeare. Maureen Dowd wrote on January 2, 1995, in the *Cincinnati Enquirer* that, "Shakespeare may be too white, too male, and too dead for Georgetown, but there is no greater writer about politics than Shakespeare." Even Shakespeare is being suppressed because his plays are not politically correct vis-à-vis "race, class, and gender." The left wingers in academia and the news media are destroying traditional education as we have known it. They have replaced it with left wing, politically correct, indoctrination.

An example of this was the controversy over the National History Standards. John Leo called it "The Hijacking of American History." Leo pointed out that the National History Standards excluded Orville and Wilbur Wright. The Wright brothers who invented the airplane were suppressed from the U.S. history standards, because there were too many dead, white, male inventors. There needs to be more room made for diversity. Prentice-Hall's U.S. history textbook for high school students, *A History of the United States*, published in 2002, does not include Orville or Wilbur Wright. And the worst part of this story is that Daniel J. Boorstin claims to be one of the authors of this textbook. His name appears on the cover. How could a man who wrote a book about "Discoverers" allow his name to be on a high school U.S. History textbook that excludes Orville and Wilbur Wright? This textbook has been adopted by many public high schools all across the United States of America.

Most high school U.S history teachers assumed Boorstin's textbook would be good because Boorstin is a Harvard graduate and the former senior historian of the Smithsonian Institution.

The Smithsonian Institution in Washington D.C. had an exhibit on the Enola Gay. This was the plane that dropped an atomic bomb on Japan to end World War II. The left wing professors of history at the Smithsonian who wrote the explanatory material for the exhibit claim that it was racism that motivated President Truman to drop the bomb on Japan. They also claimed that the war could have been won just as easily by America without having to drop the bomb.

The left wing lies of the Enola Gay exhibit infuriated conservative patriotic congressmen and members of the Veterans of Foreign Wars and the American Legion. These patriotic groups pointed out that more Germans were killed in the firebombing of Dresden than Japanese were killed at Hiroshima or Nagasaki. Racism had nothing to do with it. They also pointed out that Truman's decision to drop the atomic bomb saved half a million American lives by preventing the need for an invasion of the Japanese home islands.

Congress threatened to cut off funding for the Smithsonian if they did not clean up their act. Finally, they re-wrote the exhibit to give a more balanced view instead of the previous left wing indoctrination they had tried to foist upon the American people.

Yet even today much of the history section of the Smithsonian has not changed its left wing ways. In 2002, the Smithsonian turned down a gift of $38 million from Catherine B. Reynolds.

Why did they turn it down? Because the gift had one string attached. That string was that the money must be used to create an exhibit that displays and promotes 100 American heroes and their individual accomplishments. Rupert Cornwell wrote in the British newspaper *The Independent*, "the basic philosophy for the exhibit -- the power of the individual to make a difference -- is the antithesis of that espoused by many within the Smithsonian bureaucracy, which is that only movements and institutions make a difference, not individuals. There is no way to reconcile these diametrically opposed philosophical viewpoints". John Leo in his column on October 31, 1994, called this type of thing "the politically correct attack on heroism". Many of these left wing historians still hold fast to the Marxist economic interpretation of history. Marxism survives in Mainland China, North Korea, Cuba, Harvard University, and the elite "mainstream" news media. Why do you think Harvard felt the need to ban the ROTC from its campus? Did you know that to this very day they have not invited it back? The Harvard elite sees American military heroes who fought Communism in Vietnam or anywhere else as "baby killers". Doctors who perform partial birth abortions are seen as heroes of women's reproductive rights.

Another example of this left wing bias in modern American education is that the professors who wrote the College Board's Advanced Placement test in U.S. history banned all military history questions from the test. They do not want young people to study military history. Their hatred for the U.S. Military is so deep and passionate that they do not consider it important enough to put on a U.S. history test in which high school students compete for college credits. The Princeton Review for the A.P. U.S. history test tells the high school students, "The A.P. U.S. history exam doesn't ask about military history." They believe that decisive battles should be ignored while liberal social movements should be emphasized.

The field of medicine is not even immune to the disease known as political correctness. The ancient Greek physician Hippocrates wrote an oath known as the Hippocratic Oath. Medical doctors upon graduating from U.S. medical schools were to swear an oath of allegiance to the ethics contained therein. One of the lines of the Hippocratic Oath forbids abortions. And another line forbids euthanasia. Therefore many medical schools today are banning the oath or suppressing and editing out the "politically incorrect" lines. The goal of "The Medical Professionalism Project" is to abolish the Hippocratic Oath altogether and replace it with the politically correct document entitled "The Charter on Medical Professionalism." This new charter does not speak out against abortion and euthanasia the way the Hippocratic Oath did. The history of Hippocrates and the specifics of his oath are now being suppressed.

Why is there liberal bias in the media and academia? Have there been any studies that document liberal domination of the media and academia? In 1996 the Freedom Forum and the Roper Center surveyed journalists concerning their voting habits. They discovered that in the 1992 Presidential election 89% of journalists voted for Bill Clinton, while just 43% of the general public voted for Clinton. This disparity is disturbing.

In 1985, the *Los Angeles Times* conducted a survey, which found that 82% of journalists were pro-abortion, while only 49% of the general public was pro-abortion. They also found that 78% of journalists are for more gun control, even though less than half the general public is for more gun control. In addition, their research showed that only 4% of journalists that work in Washington, D.C. as bureau chiefs and Congressional correspondents, are registered Republicans.

This left wing dominance is found not only in the media, but also in academia. In 2002, the *American Enterprise* magazine did a random survey of 172 professors at Cornell University. They found that 166 of those professors were registered Democrat or Green Party ("parties of the left"), while only 6 of those professors were registered Republican or Libertarian ("parties of the right"). Those results were the norm at all the colleges they surveyed. For example, at Stanford University the ratio was 151 left wing professors to only 17 conservative professors. At the University of Colorado-Boulder, there were 116 registered with the "left" and only 5 registered with the "right". At the University of California-San Diego there were 99 left wing professors and only 6 conservative professors.

This type of imbalance was found practically across the board in academia and the media. With statistics like this, how could a sane person believe that the media and academia have no bias and therefore report to us only the truth, the whole truth, and nothing but the truth, so help them God?

The leftists who control most of the media and academia have every right to believe and vote as they wish; that is not the problem. The problem is their lack of full disclosure. The problem is that they try to deceive the general public by portraying themselves as objective, neutral, observers and reporters of the truth. This is a big lie that they have perpetrated for years. It is time for this lie to be exposed. It is time for the truth to be revealed.

There is a limited amount of time in a collegiate lecture and in a nightly news broadcast. There is a limited amount of space in a newspaper. Frequently the conscious or unconscious liberal bias of the journalists and professors manifests itself in what is omitted from the lecture, broadcast, or newspaper. This book is an attempt to fill in some of those gaps and to reveal facts that were omitted because of liberal bias.

If the evidence is not suppressed, widely held paradigms could be destroyed. There have been many examples of this in the past. Prior to 1871 almost all highly educated people believed that Homer's city of Troy as described in *The Iliad*, was 100 percent fictional. The left wing anti-hero elite in academia, science, and journalism believed that Homer was a liar at worst or a spinner of fictitious tales at best. Troy as a city never actually existed. If you believed it did exist then you must be a kook or a madman. This orthodox view seemed to be set in stone. The paradigm seemed to be unassailable. The left wing elite academics felt good about their superior knowledge and looked down upon the masses, especially those members of the masses who still believed in romantic "fairy tales" of old. They also looked down upon people who were not professional academics and archeologists. They had contempt for individual mavericks that believed in ideas that did not fit within the accepted paradigm.

One-man stepped forward and destroyed their paradigm with a pickax. His name was Heinrich Schliemann. He was a businessman and an amateur archeologist. He read Homer and believed Homer. He dug on the hill at Hisarlick, in present day Turkey, which is where he thought the Iliad told him to dig. He found nine cities on top of one another like layers of a massive wedding cake. Troy 6A was Homer's Troy. It had a weaker west wall just as Homer had described it in *The Iliad.* It had the holy tower of Ilios as Homer said it would. It had walls slanted at a peculiar angle just as Homer had described it. Schliemann had destroyed the left wing and anti-heroic paradigm. Now virtually all highly educated people believe Troy actually did exist.

For many years, highly educated left wing academics and most psychologists and psychiatrists subscribed to Freudian psychology. The orthodox view of the psychological profession was Freudian. Sigmund Freud taught us that nearly all psychological problems have a sexual element. The Oedipus complex, the idea that one wants to have sex with one's mother and kill one's father as described by Jim Morrison of the Doors in the song "This Is The End," was supposed to explain our current mental state. The way to help mentally ill people was to put them on the couch and psychoanalyze them. This was known as Freudian talk therapy.

Today Freudian psychoanalysis is considered ridiculous by the psychological profession. Freud has been dismissed as a quack whose research was nonscientific and highly suspect. Today the new paradigm is psychopharmacology. It's the brain chemistry, which can be fixed by drugs. It is not suppressed sexual urges that can be coped with by psychoanalysis.

How did the paradigm shift from Freud to psychopharmacology? Tom Wolfe says, "The demise of Freudianism can be summed up in a single word: lithium." John Cade discovered in 1949 that lithium could temporarily cure the problems associated with manic depression.

Another paradigm that has dominated much of the globe and many intellectual minds over the last eighty years is that of Marxism. The Marxist paradigm was decimated in 1989 with the destruction of the Berlin Wall. The Marxist paradigm was virtually destroyed with the collapse of Communism in the Soviet Union in1991. What other left wing paradigms may fall?

Let us now uncover eight new profound examples of suppressed history. These are eight new examples of paradigms that are about to collapse but are currently being upheld by the suppression of information. The left wing is doing its best to suppress the information contained within this book. They know that if this suppressed history were circulated to the masses it would shatter many left wing academic orthodoxies. It would strike a crippling blow to the political correctness movement, which seeks to keep the people in a dark cave of ignorance and not allow them into the light of day.

Be forewarned that when one is led out of the dark cave and into the light of day, one's eyes must adjust to the brightness of the light. Plato taught us this in his book *The Republic*: "But a nobler manner of education there could not be."

Can you handle the truth? If not, don't read this book.

2
Custer at Gettysburg

"When the primordial sentiments of a people weaken, there invariably follows a decline of belief in the hero. To see the significance of this, we must realize that the hero can never be a relativist."

-Richard Weaver

When I was a little boy, my father took me to the battlefield at Gettysburg, and one of the ranger-historians impressed something upon me that I had not fully realized. It concerned the great Confederate cavalry commander James Ewell Brown Stuart, usually referred to as Jeb Stuart. General Stuart was late getting to the battlefield at Gettysburg. He arrived at Gettysburg on the night of the second day. General Lee said, "General Stuart, you are here at last." Then they talked about plans for the battle on the third day. General Lee ordered General Stuart to sneak around the Union flank and wreak havoc in the Union rear while Pickett's infantry hit the center of the Union line. General Stuart thought he could accomplish this and make everything right. His cavalry outnumbered the Union cavalry. His "Invincibles" were better horsemen and better fighters. They had never lost a battle. But one thing went wrong. He ran head-on into another great American legend. For the Union rear at Gettysburg was protected by the cavalry of a 23-year-old General by the name of George Armstrong Custer.

Ted Turner, in his film *Gettysburg* portrays Robert E. Lee as a senile old fool who made all the wrong decisions. This is not true. Robert E. Lee was a brilliant military tactician and strategist. He proved this time and again by defeating numerically superior Union forces. At Chancellorsville, Lee sent Stonewall Jackson's "Foot Cavalry" on a flanking movement to attack the Union rear, while Lee himself held the center. It worked perfectly, and the numerically inferior Confederate Army of Northern Virginia won the day once again.

On the first day of the Battle of Gettysburg, Lee wanted to turn the Union right flank. Lee ordered General Ewell to take Culps Hill. Lee issued this order early, when there were not many Union troops occupying Culps Hill. Ewell hesitated. He waited many hours until the Union brought in reinforcements on Culps Hill. By the time Ewell attacked Culps Hill it was too late. The Confederates were repulsed. The Confederate failure to take Culps Hill on the first day was the fault of Ewell. It was not Lee's fault. If Ewell had carried out Lee's orders promptly, the Confederates may very well have won the Battle of Gettysburg. For they would have controlled the high ground on the Union's right flank, which was Culps Hill.

On the second day of the Battle of Gettysburg, Lee ordered Longstreet to take Little Round Top in order to turn the Union's left flank. Longstreet was ordered by Lee to do this first thing in the morning. Longstreet hesitated and procrastinated. Longstreet finally attacked Little Round Top at 4p.m. By this time Little Round

Top was reinforced by Union troops. Longstreet failed to take Little Round Top. The fault for this was Longstreet's, not Lee's. The Ted Turner film portrays Longstreet as a young, brilliant military strategist making all the right decisions, and Lee as a senile old man making all the wrong decisions. This is completely false. Longstreet could have taken Little Round Top if he had attacked first thing in the morning as Lee had ordered.

Ewell and Longstreet could not replace Stonewall Jackson. Stonewall was mortally wounded at Chancellorsville. Lee was right when he said, "Stonewall has lost his left arm and I have lost my right." Stonewall was Lee's right hand man, one who could be depended upon in a tough situation. Gettysburg proved that Ewell was no Stonewall Jackson. Gettysburg proved that Longstreet was no Stonewall Jackson.

On the third day of the Battle of Gettysburg, Lee decided to reenact his great victory at Chancellorsville. Lee would use a variation of the plan he used to win at Chancellorsville. Lee could not utilize Stonewall Jackson for the flanking movement, because he was dead. Lee could not count on Longstreet or Ewell for this daring plan. Lee needed men on horseback to carry out this huge flanking attack. Lee chose Jeb Stuart and "Stuart's Invincibles," a cavalry unit that had never been defeated.

Lee's plan was as follows: General Pickett's Infantry would strike the Union front at the same time General Stuart's cavalry would strike the Union rear. These two pincers supporting one another had the potential of breaking in half the

Union position at Gettysburg. This would have brought about a tremendous Confederate victory, the destruction of the army of the Potomac, and a Confederate march on Washington, D.C., which was actually south of Gettysburg, Pennsylvania.

Said Stuart in his report of the events of that day: "On the morning of July 3, pursuant to instructions from the commanding General, I hoped to effect a surprise upon the enemy's rear."

On July 3rd, 1863, the third day of the Battle of Gettysburg, General Custer spotted Stuart's advance and decided to attack. Jeb Stuart's forces outnumbered Custer and his Wolverines (Custer's men were from Michigan, hence the name Wolverines) but this did not deter Custer. Custer personally led the cavalry charge. He yelled to his men, "Come on you Wolverines." Custer charged Stuart's "Invincibles." Jeb Stuart, also like Custer, wanted the force of momentum to be on his side. Therefore both men charged their cavalry toward one another. David F. Riggs, in his book *East of Gettysburg-Custer vs. Stuart*, wrote, "As the Wolverines and Invincibles met, there was a sudden and violent collision as many horses in the front ranks turned end over end crushing their riders beneath them. The clashing of sabers, the firing of pistols, the demands for surrender, and the screams of combatants filled the air. Men and horses fell in dense heaps, but the First Michigan under Custer managed to part the Rebels like a wedge, making charge and counter charge. Custer's horse was shot out from underneath him, and while on the ground he was singed by a bullet in his shoulder. Bloody and bruised, yet unbowed, Custer leaped into an empty saddle and reentered the fray."

When the Confederate cavalry General Wade Hampton was wounded, "General Custer felled Hampton's standard bearer, and the Confederate General's flag was captured." The Union cavalry under Custer had won the day. Jeb Stuart and the Confederate cavalry had lost. Custer stopped Stuart from being able to break through to the Union rear.

As Robert M. Utley writes in the introduction to *A Cavalryman with Custer*, "General George A. Custer prevented Stuart from smashing into the Union rear at the very moment Pickett's Charge faltered at the copse of trees that came to define the high water mark of the Confederacy."

D.A. Kinsley wrote, on page 154 of his book, *Custer-Favor the Bold*, "Custer succeeded in turning the tide at Gettysburg, by saving Meade from a disastrous rear attack by Stuart."

I recently revisited the battlefield at Gettysburg, in order to do some further research for this book. I walked the East Cavalry Battlefield. I saw a monument there, which was dedicated to Custer and the Michigan Cavalry Brigade. I looked up at the monument and saw Custer's face. The face looked like that of a gambler with nerves of steel, who was ready, willing, and able to go for broke even against overwhelming odds.

It was the face of an adventurer who was willing to risk his life at every turn. It was the face of a man who personally led 21 cavalry charges in the Civil War and had 11 horses shot out from under him. It was the face of a man willing to charge the enemy, even when he was greatly outnumbered. It was the face of courage.

What Custer did at Gettysburg to preserve the Union cannot be more aptly stated then by the inscription on that monument. It states:

> "This monument marks the field where the Michigan Cavalry Brigade, under its gallant leader, General George Custer, rendered signal and distinguished service in assisting to defeat the further advance of a numerically superior force under the Confederate General J.E.B. Stuart who, in conjunction with Pickett's Charge upon the center, attempted to turn the right flank of the Union Army at the critical hour of the conflict on the afternoon of July 3, 1863."

George Armstrong Custer played a crucial role in the Union victory at Gettysburg, which was the turning point battle in the Civil War.

Custer's crucial role in the Union victory at Gettysburg has been suppressed. Ted Turner's film *Gettysburg* starring Tom Berenger as Longstreet, and Martin Sheen as Robert E. Lee, completely censors Custer from the Battle. Custer is ignored. By watching this film one would get the impression that Custer played no role whatsoever in the Union victory at Gettysburg.

Bill Diehl of ABC radio said that Ted Turner's film *Gettysburg* was "A towering achievement, it explodes on the screen in all its horror and heroism." It showed all of its heroism except for Custer's heroism. Custer must be banned from positive publicity, because he fought Indians, and today this is not deemed to be politically correct.

Most high school and collegiate U.S. history textbooks fail to mention Custer's crucial role at the Battle of Gettysburg. One could read all the public high school U.S. history textbooks and come away with the impression that Custer played absolutely no role in the Union victory at Gettysburg. This information has been suppressed. The left wing professors who write the textbooks and the left wing artists who make the films hate Custer. Custer believed in and fought for American "Manifest Destiny," and this is anathema to the leftists in Hollywood and the Ivy League.

Custer performed at Gettysburg as if he were more than a man. At the Little Big Horn, Custer proved he was merely a man. As Shakespeare would say, "The elements were so mixed in him that nature might stand up and say to all the world, 'This was a man'."

As D.A. Kinsley said, on pages 143 and 144 of his book, *Custer Favor the Bold*, "To hate Custer is to hate the ideals of manhood." Most modern left wing professors hate Custer, and therefore they disparage him for his Indian fighting and ignore his contributions to America at the Battle of Gettysburg, because they are jealous of his machismo. They realize deep down that by comparison they are not men. These professors hate Custer for the same reasons they hate John Wayne, because John Wayne was not a politically correct wimp.

Left wing professors hate the U.S. military. Left wing professors are glad that Harvard University kicked out the R.O.T.C.

Most of these left wing professors are now committed feminists. That is why the head of the department of history is called an inanimate object, a "chair." They don't call themselves "chairmen," because they know they are not men.

These left wing professors of History and Political Science that dominate academia today are what T.S. Eliot referred to as "The Hollow Men." The charismatic figures like Columbus, Crockett, and Custer are hated by these hollow academics. These hollow chested left wing academics are glad that "Mistah Kurtz," Mr. Columbus, Mr. Crockett, and Mr. Custer, are dead. The hollow chested left wing professor's lecture "voices are quiet and meaningless as wind in dry grass." These professors no longer believe in the Biblical apocalyptic ending of this world. They only believe in Darwinian gradualism that they call uniformitarianism. Their worldview leaves no room for catastrophism. It leaves no room for military heroes and catastrophic battles of man or God. Their world ends "not with a bang but a whimper."

The great Christian intellectual C.S. Lewis said it best in his essay entitled "Men Without Chests," contained within his masterpiece *The Abolition of Man.* C.S. Lewis understood that what these left wing professors lack is a belief in objective truth. "But what is common to them all is something we cannot neglect. It is the doctrine of objective value, the belief that certain attitudes are really true, and others really false, to the kind of thing the universe is and the kind of things we are...."

Custer was a man with a chest that was stuck out and a chin that was up. He was a military man of honor. He was brave. He was courageous. C.S. Lewis understood that this was the type of man we need to praise, not bash. C.S. Lewis wrote, "And all the time-such is the tragicomedy of our situation-We continue to clamor for those very qualities we are rendering impossible. You can hardly open a periodical without coming across the statement that what our civilization needs is more 'drive,' or dynamism, or self-sacrifice, or 'creativity.' In a sort of ghastly simplicity we remove the organ and demand the function. We make men without chests and expect of them virtue and enterprise. We laugh at honor and are shocked to find traitors in our midst. We castrate and bid the gelding be fruitful."

It is a shame that Custer, a man of many Civil War victories, is known for a single defeat. I am referring to the Battle of The Little Big Horn River Valley. According to the academics, Custer "foolishly" divided his small command into three separate entities. But Custer's 211 men who were wiped out by thousands of Indians from a conglomeration of many tribes, inflicted such heavy and disproportionate casualties among the Indian warrior population in that battle, that never again would the Indians be able to mount a serious military threat to the United States and its move westward.

It seems Custer had a subconscious lust for combat. He died the warrior's death. His last stand was similar to Davy Crockett's last stand at the Alamo. Both were tactical defeats; yet both were strategic victories.

Why did Custer do such a "foolish" thing at the Little Big Horn? I believe it was because he was the supreme adventurer. The more the odds were against him, the more he enjoyed it!

3
The Death of Davy Crockett

"We need heroes. We need those people to show us the way, to show us what we can be and need to be."

-Mel Gibson

In this era of "political correctness" on American Ivy League college campuses, it is becoming more and more popular and prevalent for anti-hero, revisionist historians to rewrite history in order to destroy the traditional American heroes posthumously. Today Columbus, Custer and Crockett are all being lambasted as evil men who were not politically correct. Their hero status is being suppressed so that today's young people learn only the liberal revisionist version of their stories.

Many of our young people today learn their U.S. History through films. There have been two famous films on Davy Crockett. The original Mr. Walt Disney made the first film in 1955 in which Fess Parker played the role of Crockett. The second was Mr. John Wayne's film in 1960 in which John Wayne played the role of Crockett. Both of these films were patriotic, pro-Texan, and pro-American. That was because Mr. Walt Disney and Mr. John Wayne were both patriotic Americans who did not subscribe to what today is called "political correctness." They both portrayed Crockett as an American hero, the Texans and Tennesseans as the good guys and the Mexicans under Santa Anna as the bad guys.

More recently, left wing liberal anti-hero political correctness has not only crept into academia, but it has also crept into the Alamo itself, as well as into Hollywood. The Alamo in San Antonio recently changed its introductory film for visitors. The old film portrayed the Texan defenders as the good guys and the Mexican attackers as the bad guys. The new film at the Alamo portrays both the Texans and the Mexicans as the good guys. They felt the need to bow down to the pressure of political correctness.

The new leadership at Disney is in the process of making a new Alamo feature film. It is currently scheduled to come out in April of 2004. One must understand that Walt Disney, the man, was a conservative. Since he died, the Disney Company has been taken over by politically correct liberals. They have inserted politically correct liberal bias in their corporate policies. For example, homosexual couples are given marital benefits, and this is why a conservative Christian group (The Southern Baptist Convention) decided to boycott Disney films.

An early script of this film has been reviewed by film critics on the World Wide Web. They say that Crockett's death in this film will be ambiguous. They also say that this film will be much more "politically correct" than the 1950's Disney film. In this new film the Texan leadership of Travis, Bowie, and Crockett will be portrayed as extremely flawed individuals whose supposed dirty laundry will be bandied about for all to see. Much of the story will be told through the eyes of a Mexican soldier. The common Mexican soldiers will be portrayed as good guys.

Disney will portray some of the Texan defenders of the Alamo as lower-class white racists. Times sure have changed.

The liberals are doing their best to destroy the reputations of Columbus, Custer, Crockett, Travis, and Bowie posthumously. They are even willing to spend millions of dollars on a film to accomplish part of their mission. But today it is not just moviemakers that want to besmirch Crockett's reputation as a military hero. Academic historians are also attacking Crockett's legendary status.

In 1975, Carmen Perry wrote a book stating that Davy Crockett surrendered at the Alamo and then was executed. In 1978, Dan Kilgore wrote a book that, like Perry's, also argued the case that Crockett surrendered and did not die fighting but was executed. Paul Andrew Hutton put forth the same argument in a book published in 1987. These three historians, Perry, Kilgore, and Hutton, promote the revisionist line that Crockett did not die in battle at the Alamo. This chapter will show you how they came to their conclusion. It will also show you the evidence, which pertains to this case. It will prove that Perry, Kilgore, and Hutton are wrong. It will prove that Davy Crockett did indeed die a heroic death in battle at the Alamo.

If Hutton is the prosecutor, his star witness, upon whom he bases the theory of his case, is Lieutenant Colonel Jose Enrique de la Pena. Hutton writes on page xxxiii of his introduction to *David Crockett, By Himself*, "Of these Mexican eyewitness accounts (of Crockett's surrender), none is more reliable than that of

Lieutenant Colonel Jose Enrique de la Pena, an officer on Santa Anna's staff. According to de la Pena, Crockett presented himself to Castrillon as a tourist who had taken refuge in the Alamo upon the approach of the Mexican army. Crockett was no soldier and in this hopeless situation an attempt to talk his way out makes perfect sense." Crockett was a soldier in the Creek Indian War and was often referred to as Colonel Crockett. If being a combat veteran does not make one a soldier, I do not know what does.

Perry, Kilgore, and Hutton all base their belief that Crockett surrendered upon three unsubstantiated premises. One, that De la Pena's diary is truthful. Two, that his diary is authentic. And three, that evidence given by witnesses on only one side of a dispute is more credible then evidence gleaned from interviewing witnesses from both sides of a dispute.

Lieutenant Colonel de la Pena is not a credible witness. First, he is a high-ranking officer on Santa Anna's staff who has a personal stake and motive to lie about the death of Davy Crockett. If he tells the truth that Crockett died in battle, it would make Crockett into a martyr and give added strength to Sam Houston and the Texan force that would try to kill him. It is not wise to make a heroic martyr out of your enemy.

Lieutenant Colonel de la Pena lacks credibility for another reason. He delivers self-serving testimony in order to save and protect himself in the contingency that Sam Houston defeats Santa Anna in the future and it comes time for the Texans to avenge the death of Crockett. Lieutenant Colonel de la Pena's testimony is that Santa Anna ordered the execution of Crockett but that he (Pena) protested it in the name of altruism and love. This is certainly a self-serving motive to lie. De la Pena said, "The commanders and officers were outraged at Santa Anna's order to execute Crockett and did not support the order, hoping that once the fury of the moment had blown over, these men would be spared."

Perry, Kilgore, and Hutton all base their belief that Crockett surrendered on the unsubstantiated premise that Jose Enrique De la Pena's diary is authentic. De la Pena's diary did not surface until 1955, a full 119 years after the battle. Alamo scholar Joseph Musso believes that Jose Enrique de la Pena's diary is a forgery. He bases this belief on an analysis by handwriting expert Charles Hamilton who stated, "I certify that I have carefully examined the document allegedly written by Jose Enrique De la Pena and find that it is a forgery by John Laflin, alias John Laffite." Laflin is known as one of the most talented and prolific forgers in American history. He also forged a letter by Alamo defender Isaac Milsaps. Both the Milsaps letter and the De la Pena diary surfaced out of the blue in 1955, over one hundred years after the fact. The Milsap letter and De la Pena diary both had handwriting anomalies that indicated they were written by the same person. These facts severely damage the case made by Perry, Kilgore, and Hutton concerning Crockett's death.

One of the key facts that destroys Hutton's revisionist thesis and theory of the case is that, as Hutton admitted himself, "All of the accounts of

Crockett's surrender are by Mexicans." To accept these accounts as true at face value is "akin to accepting only Union accounts of the Battle of Gettysburg." Those are Hutton's words, words in which he admits the weakness of his case. The prosecution's witnesses lack credibility.

The most credible form of evidence backs up the thesis that Crockett died a heroic death in battle at the Alamo. That evidence includes corroborating witnesses from both sides of the dispute, Mexican and Texan, and corroboration from witnesses of all races and sexes represented at the Alamo.

On page xxxii of Hutton's introduction, Captain Rafael Soldana, a Mexican, said, "A tall man, with flowing hair, was seen firing from the same place on the parapet during the entire siege. He wore a buckskin suit and a cap all of a pattern entirely different from those worn by his comrades. This man would kneel or lie down behind the low parapet, rest his long gun and fire, and we all learned to keep at a good distance when he was seen to make ready to shoot. He rarely missed his mark, and when he fired he always rose to his feet and calmly reloaded his gun seemingly indifferent to the shots fired at him by our own men. He had a strong, resonant voice and often railed at us, but as we did not understand English we could not comprehend the import of his words further than they were defiant. This man I later learned was known as 'Kwockey.'"

Does this Crockett sound like a man who would surrender and pass himself off as a tourist to surviving Mexican troops that have seen him kill many Mexicans? I think not!

On page 138 of Lon Tinkle's book, *The Alamo*, which was originally titled *13 Days to Glory*, states that, "Now, like Travis, Crockett died outdoors, where he wished to be. When the firing was over, he and his men were found at their assigned post near the stockade fence. In his hand was 'Old Betsy', his favorite rifle, the inscription down the length of the barrel reading 'Presented by the young men of Philadelphia to the Honorable Davy Crockett.' In mute testimony to a man whose marksmanship was legendary, the greatest concentration of Mexican bodies is said to have been found around Crockett's body. Santa Anna's cook, Ben, said the fifty-year-old frontiersman was surrounded by 'no less than sixteen Mexican corpses' and that one lay across his body with the 'huge knife of Davy buried in the Mexicans bosom to the hilt.' Travis's Joe reported that 'Crockett and a few of his friends were found together with twenty-four of the enemy around them.' Others set the figure at seventeen."

Santa Anna's cook, Ben, a Mexican, and Travis's Joe, an African-American, both testify to the fact that they saw Crockett's dead body and the 17 or so Mexicans he had killed around him. Tinkle also reports in his book that, "Ben, Santa Anna's cook who had often seen Congressmen Crocket in Washington, saw him a last time after the battle, his coonskin cap lying at his side." If Crockett were executed, the Mexicans would not have put a Mexican on Davy's lap with "Davy's huge knife in the Mexican's bosom to the hilt."

They would not have had time to move the bodies anyway. The multi-racial corroboration of evidence is building.

The last two witnesses are Susanna Dickinson, who was a white Texan woman, and Sergeant Felix Nunez, who was a Hispanic Mexican soldier. On page xxxv, Hutton admits that Susanna Dickinson was the only adult Anglo survivor of the Alamo, and that she saw Crockett's dead body right after the battle and made comments recorded on paper about what she saw. Both Hutton and Tinkle write that Susanna Dickinson said, "I recognized Colonel Crockett lying dead and mutilated between the church and the two story barrack building and even remembered seeing his peculiar cap lying by his side."

Not only Lon Tinkle, author of *13 Days of Glory*, backs up and supports the hero thesis, but so does a book entitled *Roll Call at the Alamo* by Rosenthal and Groneman. They tell in great detail about the evidence already put forward, but they also add one more witness to the case. His name is Sergeant Felix Nunez; he related that Crocket did indeed die in battle. Sergeant Felix Nunez talked about his eyewitness account of "the heroic death of a tall American dressed in buckskins and wearing a fur cap." The weight of the evidence is overwhelming. It all points to one conclusion: Crockett died a heroic death in battle.

The anti-heroic, revisionist thesis is based on faulty and biased evidence, which comes entirely from one side, which is engaged in an ethnically charged war. This thesis, put forth by

Paul Andrew Hutton, stated that Davy Crockett surrendered and then was executed at the Alamo. Hutton claims Crockett tried to pass himself off as a tourist strolling through town. An innocent third party! How preposterous! Hutton, on page xxxv in the introduction to *David Crockett, By Himself*, states about Crockett, "that he did not fall at the height of battle. Such a death would have been out of character with his life. He was no warrior chieftain-no combination of Beowulf and Roland."

After taking into account all the evidence, the credibility of the individual witnesses, and multi-racial evidence corroborated by members of both sides in the Texan War of Independence, it is clear to see that Davy Crockett died in battle at the Alamo. It is also clear to see that Hutton is wrong. Crockett does deserve his legendary military status. Davy Crockett was a combination of the traditional heroes, Beowulf and Roland. For Davy Crockett fought and fell in the name of God with glory, guns, and guts. Anti-hero academics can attempt to suppress the true stories about heroes in American history, but the truth will win out in the end.

Postscript to this story: New evidence has emerged that lends even more credence to the idea that the de la Pena diary is a forgery. In November of 2002, Bill Groneman pointed out that the diary contains the phrase "crimes against humanity." This phrase was not coined until the 20th century, and de la Pena died in the 19th century. It doesn't add up.

My Visit to the Alamo

In order to do some further research for this book, I personally visited the Alamo in February of 2003. I was teaching U.S. History, but I had a three-day weekend because of the President's Day Holiday. I flew down to San Antonio, Texas and stayed three nights in the Westin. My hotel was right on the river walk, which was quite beautiful, and only a few blocks from the Alamo itself.

The first thing I learned on this trip was that the *History Channel* now controls the introductory film for visitors on the Alamo grounds. (Michael Eisner's Disney Corporation owns both The *History Channel* and *Touchstone Pictures*, and Eisner is well known for his leftwing politics.) When I went into the little room to see the film I was shocked by two sins of omission committed by this film. First, it did not describe the death of Crockett, and secondly, it did not describe the death of Bowie. The film was eerily silent on these two important issues. It did describe the death of Travis, but not Crockett or Bowie. At that moment I thought something wasn't right. Ok, maybe they dodged the controversy about Crockett, but why didn't they describe the death of Bowie? Later I found out the shocking answer to this question.

This introductory film at the Alamo is 15 minutes in length. It emphasizes the Tejanos (The Mexicans who fought with and for the Texans against Santa Anna) especially Gregoria Esparza. It does say that Santa Anna showed the red flag of no quarter to the Alamo defenders, and it mentions the fact that the Mexican bugler played a call of no quarter immediately prior to the attack. This begs the question: Why would Crockett surrender to the Mexicans when he knows full well no quarter will be given, and he will be executed anyway? It doesn't make sense. It doesn't add up. In Germany in 1945, Germans were willing to surrender to American and British troops, because they knew they would be given quarter, but they were not willing to surrender to Russian troops because they knew that the Communists would not give any quarter, but instead would torture and kill them. One does not surrender to an enemy that has already advertised the fact that it will give no quarter. One fights to the death against such an enemy.

The film ends by giving credit to Clara Driscoll and the Daughters of the Republic of Texas for buying and preserving the Alamo chapel and long barracks. If Clara Driscoll knew that the Alamo itself had been taken over by revisionist historians who preach within its walls that Crockett surrendered to the Mexicans and did not fight to the end, she would turn over in her grave. But that is exactly what has happened.

After the film, I walked into the long barracks at the Alamo and was struck by the large quotations on the wall. I counted the quotations from the different participants and their frequency. Olivares 1, Smithwick 1, Austin 1, Berlandier 1, Ham 1, Blount 1, Ruiz 1, Navarro 1, Bryan 1, Milam 1, Beretta 1, William F. Gray 1, Caro 1, Deaf Smith 1, Olmsted 1, Newcomb 1, Dickinson 1, Juan Seguin 2, Jose Enrique De la

Pena 3, Santa Anna's Cook Ben 0, Rafael Soldana 0, Sgt. Felix Nunez 0.

The De la Pena forgery that implies Crockett surrendered is quoted on the long barrack walls in large print three times, while other people are quoted once or not at all. Those who say Crockett fought heroically to the end are either not quoted at all or are quoted once on an irrelevant topic far removed from the topic of Crockett's death. This is clearly selective use of evidence to bolster the importance and credibility of the De la Pena document.

Next, I went into the Alamo chapel and talked to an historian who was employed by the Alamo as an expert. This historian was one of the two that I met on this trip whose job it was to lecture the tourists on the battle from within the walls of the chapel. After his speech, I asked him about Crockett's death. He said that Crockett surrendered and that this was proven by the De la Pena document and supported eloquently, and in his mind persuasively, by Dr. James E. Crisp, a history professor at North Carolina State University. I responded to this by stating that Bill Groneman wrote a book entitled *Defense of a Legend*, which proves that the De la Pena diary is a forgery and that Crockett did indeed die fighting at the Alamo. I asked him what he thought about Groneman's arguments. His response was shocking. He said, "James Crisp is a real historian; Groneman is not a real historian." I said, "What do you mean by that?" He responded by saying, "Groneman does not have a Doctorate in history nor is he a professor of history at a university. He is just a New York City fireman." I said, "Wait a minute, some of the greatest historians and scholars have been so called amateurs who lacked a formal PhD. Schliemann found Troy, but he had no degree in archeology, and Einstein was merely a patent clerk when he discovered that $E=MC^2$. He did not at that time have a PhD, nor was he a professor." I told him research merely takes time, and genius is God given. Many comets are named after amateur astronomers who discovered them. I told him that some of the best minds work better outside the confines of academia. He had no response. We shook hands and ended the discussion immediately. We would agree to disagree.

The fact is that Groneman has written three books on the Alamo, *Defense of a Legend*, *Roll Call At the Alamo*, and *Death of a Legend.* Groneman knows more about the death of Crockett than any living man. Groneman is a New York City Fire Department Captain who pulled his fireman friends' bodies from the wreckage and rubble on 9-11-01. Groneman is an American hero in his own right. Groneman's job is to protect us from fire; his hobby is to protect Crockett's reputation from fire. The leftwing academic historians are, figuratively speaking, arsonists whose mission in life is to burn down American heroes until they are all killed off in a conflagration that destroys Western Civilization. Many of these professors are nothing more than liberal masochists who subscribe to the philosophy of Nihilism. For most leftists are inherently anti-God, anti-family, anti-country, anti-hero, anti-military, and anti-Western Civilization. They are hypocrites, because they suckle on the fruits of Western Civilization, but they constantly attack it in their writings. They also criticize the heroes: police officers, firemen, and the soldiers who protect and allow their civilization to flourish in an orderly manner. That a professor of history at the Alamo would say, "He's only a New York City Fireman" after 9-11-01 is proof positive of my point.

Another historian I talked to at the Alamo, the following day, was less dogmatic than his predecessor, yet he too believed that the De la Pena diary was authentic and accurate. He very politely discussed the different views with me concerning Crockett's death. When he finished, I said, "What's going to be next on this slippery slope? Are they going to say that Bowie was a coward who did not die fighting? Is that going to be next?" His reply shocked me. He said, " That has already happened. Many historians are now arguing that Bowie died shortly before the Mexican attack citing Madam Candelaria's account, and others are saying that Bowie 'died like a woman, almost hidden under a mattress' based upon an 1836 newspaper account by an unidentified Mexican soldier." One Mexican said Bowie died like a "coward," and now for the first time this is being believed and preached by academic historians. All the evidence that points to Bowie fighting to the end is conveniently omitted and the few pieces of testimony that portray him as a coward are trumpeted for all to hear, as the definitive account, within the leftwing of American academia.

Next, I went into the Alamo's bookstore. I perused the books on the shelves and, conveniently enough, none of Bill Groneman's books were there. Maybe they were banned because they are patriotic and not politically correct. By this time the suppression of information at the Alamo itself is making me sick to my stomach. I wondered if Sara Driscoll was turning over in her grave.

There was a male archeologist/author who was selling his books from a makeshift table within the bookstore itself. He did an archeological study on the Alamo grounds and was hawking his book about it. I asked him to enlighten me on the question of Crockett's death. He preached that Crockett surrendered and that De la Pena's diary was authentic and accurate. And in the course of his lecture he told me and those around us listening in that the U.S. did a terrible injustice to the Mexican people by taking over all that land in the southwest by both the Texan War for Independence and the Mexican War. He preached vociferously against "American Imperialism." He equated American "Manifest Destiny" with the Nazi idea of "lebensraum." I said to him, "American Manifest Destiny is not the equivalent of Nazi lebensraum, because Nazis took over land in the east and used parts of it to exterminate millions of innocent people in concentration camps. The U.S. took land in the west and used it to give people more freedom and opportunity than they had access to anywhere else in the world." I told him that the fact that Mexicans to this day vote with their feet to cross the border and come into the United States proves my point. People don't willingly move to places that will lower their standard of living and/or put them in a concentration camp and kill them. He was dumbfounded by the fact that I had the audacity to confront and contradict his left-wing anti-American diatribe. He didn't seem accustomed to being challenged on his views. He got flustered. I knew I had won the debate, for it was reflected in the faces and comments of the people listening in around us. As I walked back to the hotel, I felt enthusiastic about the debate in which I had been engaged, but then I felt saddened by the fact that there wasn't one "expert" that I met at the Alamo that was not brainwashed by the academic and political left.

The leftwing academics claim to believe in racial diversity, but most of them hate Justice Clarence Thomas and Miguel Estrada and believe that they should not be allowed to serve as federal judges. The leftwing academics claim to believe in diversity of thought, but they do their best to ban conservative thought and suppress any evidence that does not conform to their narrow leftwing world-view.

At the Alamo today the following information is suppressed (This information is also suppressed from the History Channel's documentary entitled "The Alamo" which aired on national television on 3-3-03 and 3-4-03.):

A Mexican soldier who fought at the Alamo by the name of Sergeant Felix Nunez said the following about Crockett's death: "He was a tall American of rather dark complexion and had on a long buckskin coat and a round cap without any bill, made out of fox skin with the long tail hanging down his back. This man apparently had a charmed life. Of the many soldiers who took deliberate aim at him and fired, not one ever hit him. On the contrary, he never missed a shot. He killed at least eight of our men, besides wounding several others. This being observed by a lieutenant who had come in over the wall, he sprang at him and dealt him a deadly blow with his sword, just above the right eye, which felled him to the ground, and in an instant he was pierced by not less than 20 bayonets." You cannot find that quote at the Alamo today, but you can find it on page 35 of an out of print book by Bill Groneman entitled *Roll Call at the Alamo.*

Another quotation that seems to have been banned from the Alamo and the *History Channel*, was put forth by Enrique Esparza in which he stated, "[Crockett] was everywhere during the siege and personally slew many of the enemy with his rifle, his pistol and knife. He fought hand to hand. He clubbed his rifle when they closed in on him and knocked them down with its stock until he was overwhelmed by numbers and slain. He fought to the last breath. He fell immediately in front of the large double doors, which he defended with the force that was by his side. Crockett was one of the few who were wide-awake when the final crisis and crash came. When he died there was a heap of slain in front and on each side of him. These he had all killed before he finally fell on the top of the heap." (I found this quotation on page 110 of Bill Groneman's book *Defense of a Legend.*)

Professor Paul Andrew Hutton, one of the leaders of the movement that wants to destroy Crockett's heroic reputation, bragged that he wanted to "dismantle" Crockett in order to free himself "from the shackles of childhood hero worship and prove once and for all my maturity and credibility as a scholar." According to the political left that controls much of academia, to believe in heroes is immature and any one that does believe in heroes has no credibility within their hallowed halls. Therefore, the only people willing to defend Crockett are outside of the ivory tower of academia; they include Bill Groneman, a New York Fire Captain, Thomas Lindley, an independent researcher from Austin, Texas, and novelist Steve Harrigan, who wrote *Gates of the Alamo.* All the PhD professors are forced to tow the leftwing line or else they will be blacklisted and ostracized within the confines of academia, which demands conformity of thought.

In this politically correct academic climate, Professor Paul Andrew Hutton went on to brag that he "wrote blistering articles debunking George Custer and a prizewinning biography of General Phil Sheridan that had not one good word to say about the main subject." It should all start to tie together now, Crockett, Custer, and the need for the political left to destroy traditional American heroes. (Page 43-Groneman-*Defense of a Legend*)

Leftwing revisionist historians will not stop with the destruction of one American hero. They feel an intense desire to destroy the reputations of all American heroes who were not politically correct. They now quote from the so-called Sanchez-Navarro journal, which says that, "Bowie died like a coward." They suppress all evidence to the contrary. A man famous for his knife fighting is now turned into a coward. In the leftwing world of the academic ivory tower good is bad and bad is good, up is down and down is up. It makes *Alice in Wonderland* look normal. It makes the naked Emperor appear to be fully dressed. (Page 103-Groneman-*Defense of a Legend*.)

The politically correct academics also suppress the facts, which prove that the De la Pena diary is a forgery. The forger John Laflin aka John Laffite liked to forge historic documents concerning Alamo defenders and pirates. In one forged document he drew a sketch of the pirate Laffite; in another document he drew a sketch of William B. Travis. Groneman pointed out on page 105 of *Defense of a Legend* that Travis' face in the sketch looked almost identical to Laffite's face in the proven forgery. It looks as if they were twin brothers or else they were drawn by the same forger, i.e. John Laflin. Groneman shows the pictures side by side. The so-called Alamo academics accept the Travis document as real but the pirate experts dismiss the Laffite sketch as a forgery. It doesn't add up.

The famous American forger John Laflin had within his possession many famous people's signatures, including Crockett's. The "Laffite Journal" and the "De la Pena Diary" have striking similarities, as if they were written by the same person, i.e. John Laflin. For instance, this quotation is found in the Laffite journal:

> "At one time I did all I could to save that same nation from complete annihilation in order to preserve the liberty founded on that most sacred document, the Declaration of Independence,

> *without receiving any compensation for myself.*"

De la Pena's diary states,

> "*....who expects no compensation...*if in bringing forth my notes I accomplish the noble objectives I have pursued in vindicating the honor of this unfortunate nation."

Laffite's journal and De la Pena's diary both say that the dead bodies on the battlefield were a "dreadful site."

Laffite experts dismiss the Laffite journal as a forgery but the Alamo "experts" enthusiastically embrace the De la Pena diary as the "most reliable" document on the Alamo battle. Hence, at the Alamo when I visited it in February of 2003, there were more quotes from De la Pena's diary on the long barracks walls than from any other single source. Sara Driscoll must be spinning in her grave.

Groneman states on page 142 of *Defense of a Legend that*, "Forgers rely on collecting old, blank paper from books published in the same period." Laflin was known to collect old paper. The De la Pena diary is actually a collection of loose papers of all different sizes and some of the papers have the tell tale marks on one side of having been previously bound. (Page 137-Groneman-*Defense of Legend*) The politically correct academics, when questioned about the authenticity of the De la Pena diary, say that "the paper was tested, it proved to date back to the right time period, therefore the diary is authentic." They refuse to take into account the fact that forgers collect old paper from the time period from blank pages in old books, which they cut into difference sizes and use as an authentic "canvas" for their false "painting". Only an idiot would forge an old document on brand new Mead notebook paper he bought at the corner store. I guess Marxist ideology is taught in academia but not logical thinking skills.

On page 143 of *Defense of a Legend,* Groneman points out that there is a watermark discrepancy on a piece of paper within the De la Pena diary. The letter is from De la Pena to Bernardo Gomez. The letter is dated September 5, 1825. The watermark on the paper upon which the letter was written is 1828. This proves that the De la Pena diary is a forgery.

Handwriting expert Charles Hamilton wrote a book entitled *Great Forgers and Famous Fakes.* He also took a close look at the De la Pena diary and stated, "I certify that I have carefully examined the document allegedly written by Jose Enrique De la Pena, entitled, Personal Narrative with Santa Anna in Texas, and find that it is a forgery by John Laflin, alias John Laffite. I have compared the handwriting in the personal narrative with other exemplars forged by Laffite that are illustrated in my book *Great Forgers and Famous Fakes* (pp. 122-129) and noted that the narrative bears the same characteristic script, slightly modified, that appears in his other fabrications in English, French, and Spanish."

In 1838, just two years after the battle of the Alamo took place and prior to the political correctness movement that took over academia, Chester Newell wrote a book on the Alamo. The book was entitled *History of the Revolution in Texas* (New York: Wiley and Putnam, 1838, reprint, New York: Arno Press, 1973, page 90 in reprint edition). Groneman writes on page 155 of his book *Defense of a Legend* that, "Chester Newell states that Crockett's death was as glorious as his career had been conspicuous, and that he and his companions had been found with heaps of dead around them." The politically correct revisionists feel the need to ban this information from the new textbooks, documentaries, and movies.

The academic and political left feel the need to suppress conservative speakers at academic forums. For example, a group of prominent leftwing academics that considered themselves experts on the Alamo held an academic conference at the University of Texas Center for American History in the year 2000 and refused to invite Bill Groneman and Thomas Lindley to be on the panel. Groneman and Lindley are the two leading Alamo researchers who believe Crockett fought it out to the end. Those in charge of the conference didn't want diversity of opinion and freedom of speech; they merely wanted conformity to their leftwing view that Crockett surrendered. Historian Stephen Hardin admitted that, "the deck was stacked against Groneman and Lindley." Professor James E. Crisp, the leading advocate of the De la Pena diary and the leading opponent of Crockett and Groneman's heroism, said at the conference, "Jose Enrique de la Pena died in despair, crushed by his failure to make his voice of dissent heard in the land." Dr. Hardin then exposed the emperor Dr. Crisp by saying, "Some voices were crushed today", referring to the fact that Groneman and Lindley were banned from the official panel at that conference.

In 1998, the De la Pena diary was to be auctioned off to the highest bidder. The leftwing professor James E. Crisp told the New York Times, "My greatest fear is that some right-wing nut case will put down a bunch of money and then throw it in the fireplace." In professor James E. Crisp's leftwing fantasy world, conservatives (i.e. "right-wingers") do not read books, they merely burn books.

Professor Crisp's comment proves that the Crockett controversy is not just a historical dispute, but that it is also part of a cultural war between anti-military, anti-hero leftists and pro-military/pro-hero conservatives. Remember, the anti-military leftwing academics banned the U.S. Army R.O.T.C. from the Harvard University campus. If they had gotten their way during the Cold War, America would have implemented a nuclear freeze and unilateral military disarmament, and the Communist forces would have been able to advance worldwide and take over their un-armed foe.

The Disney corporation, that now believes that two men living together sodomizing one another deserve marital benefits from their employer, is planning on releasing a film about the Alamo in April of 2004. They are planning on portraying Travis as a serial adulterer. They plan to feature Bowie as an evil slave trader, and

Crockett as a politically incorrect backwoodsman who wanted to escape but was trapped by his undeserved reputation. They claim they want to "demythologize" the three main Alamo figures. This is leftwing code for destroying the reputations of American heroes who were not politically correct by today's leftwing academic and Hollywood standards. Remember, it was the Hollywood stars that were most vocal about their opposition to President George W. Bush and General Tommy Franks' liberation of Saddam Hussein's Iraq in 2003. These same people want to destroy 4 heroes of Texas: Travis, Bowie, Crockett, and Bush.

During my trip to the Alamo in February of 2003, I learned something appalling, which, in a weird way, symbolically summed up the whole situation concerning the controversy over Crockett's death. At the Westin Hotel where I was staying, they gave away free newspapers each morning to their guests. I got out of bed on the morning of February 16, opened the door and picked up my copy of the *San Antonio Express-News*. On page 2B an article caught my eye. It was entitled "Then and Now, Historic Ozzy - Rocker has a storied past in S.A. He urinated on a monument in 1982." It was written by Scott Huddleston. It stated that on February 19, 1982, Ozzy Osbourne urinated on the Alamo Cenotaph, which was a stone monument honoring the Alamo defenders. For this disrespectful offense he was banned from San Antonio for 10 years. In 1991, he played in Austin and Dallas but was not allowed to play in San Antonio. In 1992, he donated $10,000 to the Daughters of the Republic of Texas. At that point the ban was lifted, and in October of 1992, Ozzy played once again in San Antonio, Texas.

This symbolizes the selling out of our cultural heritage. This symbolizes the vile hatred and disrespect leftwing academics, actors, and rock stars have towards traditional American heroes.

Rock star Ozzy Osbourne may have literally urinated on a monument dedicated to the heroic reputations of Travis, Bowie and Crockett, but today, following that precedent, leftists in Hollywood and academia are figuratively urinating on the heroic reputations of Travis, Bowie, and Crockett.

Culturally speaking, we today stand upon the shoulders of heroes who have come before us. We must defend these heroes or else the edifice we call our culture will collapse, and then we shall all surely fall into the darkness of the abyss.

The Disney/Touchstone 2004 Alamo Film

The new Disney Alamo film, which is currently scheduled to be released in April of 2004, is so anti-American and anti-Texan that its Director John Lee Hancock said, "I don't want my parents to have to leave the state." His parents live in Texas.

John Lee Hancock, a graduate of Baylor University in Texas, is a leftwing historical revisionist. For example, he stated that, "I think most people, even in Texas, say this battle [The Alamo] was between the United States and Mexico. But this was really a Mexican Civil War."

Why would Michael Eisner's Disney Corporation want to bankroll an anti-American, anti-Texan film on the Alamo? Why would they spend millions of dollars on a film that portrays the Mexicans as the good guys and the Americans as the bad guys? Disney studios' chairman Richard Cook said in the *L.A. Times* that, "we're making sure all viewpoints are expressed. You have to stay away from the stereotypes and not make broad judgments of any group." The *L.A. Times* said that, "clearly, the filmmakers and studio want to woo a multiethnic international audience...This means including points of view from both sides of the conflict, even if that means soft-pedaling the fact that the historical battle largely pitted one ethnic group against another." The director John Lee Hancock said, "It would be really hard to do something rah-rah jingoistic, patriotic." To Hancock, Texan and American patriotism is an evil form of "jingoism". Why is it "really hard" to do a patriotic movie on the Alamo? Could it be because it would not be politically correct according to today's leftwing Hollywood standards?

The Mexicans, for the most part, are portrayed in this movie as noble heroes. The director Hancock said that the "moral bellwether" for the forces that attacked the Alamo was General Manuel Castrillon, and the "moral bellwether" for the forces that defended the Alamo was Juan Seguin. See, unlike the Anglo Alamo defenders, Juan Seguin was without sin and was pure of heart for he was not fighting for the independence of Texas. He was fighting against Santa Anna's dictatorship, but he still wanted

Texas to be a province of Mexico under a democratic constitutional government. According to Hancock's revisionism, the Texan Anglos were fighting only to steal Mexican land and promote slavery. They were also morally corrupt individuals. Therefore, the only noble characters in this conflict, on both sides, were Mexicans.

Alamo scholar Thomas Ricks Lindley told the *Dallas Morning News*, "It's a negative treatment of Alamo defenders akin to that of Jeff Long in his book *Duel of Eagles*. The script's Anglo's are buffoons, drunks or incompetents, constantly fighting among themselves. When they go into battle, they're not fighting against Santa Anna's despotism. Instead, they are fighting to steal Mexican land for the sake of slavery." Alamo expert Lindley went on to tell the *Dallas Morning News* that Juan Seguin is falsely depicted in this movie. Lindley went on to say, "Other Mexican characters are never presented in a negative manner. Of course Santa Anna is cruel, but his motive is his love for his country, and his desire to keep Texas as part of the Mexican nation." He also said, "The portrayal of Lt. Col. Travis is especially wrong."

Lindley says the screenplay seems to have been based on *Duel of Eagles* by Jeff Long. What is Jeff Long's Alamo book like? *Publishers Weekly's* review of *Duel of Eagles*, said that it was historical revisionism that portrays Travis as a "syphilitic satyr unfit to lead men in battle" and Sam Houston as an "alcoholic and opium addict".

Does the famous Hollywood actor Dennis Quaid think he can medically diagnose dead people that he has never met? Quaid says that he thinks Sam Houston was a "bipolar, manic-depressive, alcoholic". Quaid portrays Houston as such in this new Disney Alamo film.

A background extra in the new Disney Alamo film, Bill Davis, remembers watching them shoot the scene where Crockett first arrives at the Alamo. A Texan says to Crockett, (who is played by Billy Bob Thornton), "With you here, Santa Anna would not dare come to Bexar." Crockett replied in a puzzled manner, "I thought the fighting was over…isn't it?" The point is that most traditional historians and most traditional movies on the Alamo portray Crockett as a brave man who went to Texas to fight for liberty, patriotism, and honor against the evil Mexican dictator Santa Anna. But in this new politically correct revisionist version Crockett did not come to fight; he thought the fighting was over, he came to rehabilitate his own political career because he was a selfish coward who wanted to become president of Texas. John Lee Hancock said Crockett fought not for "liberty" but for his own "political advantage." He said this on page 58 of the *Baylor Line,* Fall 2003 edition.

The *L.A. Times* says that, "this time Crockett, played by Billy Bob Thornton, is depicted as a frightened wanderer struggling to match his larger-than-life reputation for exploits that never occurred." The truth is Crockett was a highly skilled hunter, a noble Congressman who even stood up for causes that were politically unpopular and detrimental to his own political career, (i.e. he opposed Andrew Jackson's popular Indian Removal Bill), and he was a combat veteran of the Creek Indian War. He did all of that prior to going to the Alamo to fight for Texan Independence. He sacrificed his life for what Alamo commander Travis called "liberty, patriotism, and honor" in his famous letter from the Alamo. To portray Crockett as a "frightened wanderer" seeking only selfish political ambitions is an outright lie. It should be seen as an atrocity against history, against Texas, and against the United States of America.

Billy Bob Thornton, the actor who plays Crockett said in *USA Today*, "People who see this movie may say, 'Hey, wait. Davy can't be scared.' But he wasn't sure what he had gotten himself into." The truth is Davy Crockett knew exactly what he was getting himself into when he said, "You can go to hell, I'm going to Texas". For Davy Crockett's most famous quotation is, "First be sure you're right, then go ahead." Davy was right to fight for the liberation of Texas from an evil Mexican dictator. Crockett crossed the line when he decided to stay at the Alamo and die fighting instead of fleeing the Alamo and saving his life.

Davy Crockett is portrayed in the movie script as a "frightened wanderer" who wanted to escape "over the wall" in the dark of night, but felt paralyzed and trapped by his own undeserved heroic reputation. According to the *Star-Telegram* review of the script, Crockett says to Bowie, "If it was just me, simple old coon hunter from Tennessee, I could drop over the wall some night and take my chances. But this Davy Crockett feller-they're all watching him."

This movie also portrays William B. Travis as a serial adulterer and James Bowie as an evil slave trader. So much for "Victory or Death"

Travis, "knife fighting" Bowie, and "King of the wild frontier" Crockett. So much for posterity doing their memory justice. Apparently, Michael Eisner wants to destroy their reputations. I guess Roy Disney was right to resign from the Disney Corporation's Board of Directors. He wrote in his resignation letter words to the effect that Michael Eisner had destroyed the "soul" of his Uncle Walt's Company.

The truth is that "Victory or Death" Travis, "knife fighting" Bowie, "King of the wild frontier" Crockett, and "President/Governor" Houston are American heroes who fought against overwhelming odds in the name of what William Barret Travis referred to as "liberty, patriotism, and honor." They deserve our honor and respect, not a tabloid trashing of their reputations. If Mr. Walt Disney could treat the Alamo defenders with respect in 1955, and Mr. John Wayne could treat them with respect in 1960, why can't Mr. Michael Eisner and Mr. John Lee Hancock treat them with respect in 2004?

4
Women in Combat

"Almost all things have been found out but some have been forgotten."

-Aristotle

Liberals in the media have suppressed information concerning the issue of women in combat. In this chapter, I shall reveal that information. Should the United States Military lift its ban on women in combat units, such as infantry, armor, and artillery, or should the United States Military uphold the combat exclusion law that restricts women from being in the combat arms? The five key issues that define this debate are physical strength requirements, nondeployability rates, unit cohesion, precedents from history and from foreign countries, and the legal ramifications of a compulsory draft.

PHYSICAL STRENGTH

Are there significant differences between men and women in upper body strength and does it matter in today's modern military? According to Major James Wright, Chief of the Exercise Science Branch of the United States Army Fitness School, "Upper-body strength is an important component of every army task" (Mitchell, 1989). There are hundreds of manual-type tasks in the army, which require upper-body strength; for example, carrying wounded soldiers onto Medevac aircraft, setting up and tearing down of equipment in the fields, and carrying unwieldy and heavy machine gun artillery. Mitchell (1989) also reports that the Government Accounting Office (GAO) found that of the 97 female aircraft mechanics, 62 could not perform the "required tasks, such as changing aircraft tires and brakes, closing drag chute doors, breaking torque on bolts, and lifting heavy stands."

In 1993, the Presidential Commission on the Assignment of Women in the Armed Forces released a report on women in combat, which included expert testimony about the physical differences between men and women. The gist of the expert testimony was that women are on average smaller and weaker than men due to lower aerobic capacity and muscular strength.

Based upon these statistics, women should not be assigned to ground combat. Most female army recruits cannot do one pull up, and therefore cannot pull themselves up and over the basic training obstacle course wall. The Army had to reconfigure the exercise by allowing men to help lift and push these women over the wall (Gutmann, 2000). The physical standards in basic training have been lowered, but the physical rigors on the battlefield in Mogadishu, Somalia have remained constant, as Mark Bowden points out in his book entitled *Blackhawk Down.*

Blackhawk Down, by Bowden, is the account of United States Army Rangers being ambushed in Mogadishu, Somalia on October 3, 1993. A Russian made RPG shot down one of the Rangers' Black Hawk helicopters. The pilot and crew were surrounded by an armed hostile mob of thugs. Eighteen American soldiers were killed and many more badly wounded. One captured American was tortured, killed, stripped of his clothes and dragged through the streets of Mogadishu naked, as a prize for the taunting mob filling the streets. With all the high tech equipment in the world, combat still comes down to brute force on the ground, in the jungle, or in the streets.

Does this lack of upper body strength in females affect the modern military today? Does technology alleviate the need for upper body strength in today's military? Brian Mitchell (1989) reports that,

> There is no real evidence that technology has in fact reduced the need for physical strength among military men and women. What evidence there is shows that many military jobs still require more physical strength than most women possess. Technology has not affected the way many simple, unavoidable wartime tasks are performed.

While technological advances have affected all aspects of society, including the military, the fact remains: there are many jobs in the military that require physical strength, such as harnessing and moving warheads, and maneuvering large pieces of machinery. The fact that virtually all women lack the upper body strength to complete these tasks has a negative impact upon our modern military.

Even the so-called high tech job of being a jet aircraft pilot takes much physical strength and endurance. The Top Gun Naval Aviators who testified to the Presidential Commission on the Assignment of Women in the Armed Forces said that women couldn't pull as many Gs as men. G stands for the force of gravity, which weighs down upon a pilot as he turns his aircraft at high speeds. These G forces can render a pilot temporarily unconscious and as a result of that fact, they temporarily lose control of their aircraft. In a dog fight between a man and a woman, the woman would be at a distinct disadvantage because she could not push her bird to the edge of its envelope; whereas, the man could because he could pull more Gs before he passes out and loses control. This could result in the death of the female pilot and loss of a multimillion-dollar aircraft. This loss of American air power could turn the tide of a battle and cause more American infantry casualties on the ground because they lack air cover (Presidential Commission Report, 1993).

While addressing the Presidential Commission on the Assignment of Women in the Armed Forces (1993), Sergeant Major Overstreet, United States Marine Corps, recounted an event that occurred during the Vietnam War. Six North Vietnamese Army soldiers attacked a young company commander and his radio operator. They ended up in the same fighting hole physically struggling for their lives. It required great upper body strength to fight the enemy soldiers into a position whereby one could pull a knife and stab the Vietnamese soldier to death. If a female soldier had been in that foxhole that day, she may have lacked the upper body strength to fight off their attackers, which in turn would have cost her her own life, as well as jeopardized the life and limb of her fellow soldier who was depending on her.

Most female army recruits cannot throw a grenade safely outside of its bursting range (Gutmann, 2000). Consider the consequences. The flying shrapnel from the bursting grenade would not only endanger the female soldier's life, but the lives of the other soldiers in her combat unit. Major League Baseball does not recruit women to throw baseballs, the National Football League does not recruit women to throw footballs, nor should the United States military recruit women to throw grenades. To do so is an absurdity, which unnecessarily endangers the lives of our soldiers.

NONDEPLOYABILITY RATES

Are there significant differences between men and women in the amount of time they spend on the "disabled list" and cannot be deployed to do their jobs? This includes the topics of medical problems, attrition rates, and pregnancy.

Lack of physical strength contributes to another problem with women in the military: they need greater medical attention. The Report to the President, Presidential Commission on the Assignment of Women in the Armed Forces (1993) showed that "women are at a higher risk for exercise-induced injuries than men, with 2.13 times greater risk for lower extremity injuries, and 4.71 times greater risk for stress fractures." Mitchell (1989) reports, "Women in all of the services are hospitalized two to three times as often as men."

These statistics show what mankind has known since the beginning of time. Women are physically weaker than men. *The Holy Bible*, King James Version, in I Peter Chapter 3, verse 7 says this, "Likewise, ye husbands, dwell with them according to knowledge, give honour unto the wife, as unto the weaker vessel."

Another problem with women in the military is attrition. Mitchell (1989) defines attrition "as the failure to complete an enlistment contract." Attrition rates among servicewomen have been 36 percent higher than among servicemen (Mitchell, 1989). The primary reason attrition is clearly more evident among servicewomen is pregnancy. Pregnancy gives servicewomen power without fear of punishment.

Gutmann (2000) cites a July 1996 article in *Stars and Stripes*, which reported, "that in Bosnia, from December 20, 1995, when the deployment began, until July 1996, one woman had to be evacuated for pregnancy approximately every 3 days." Pregnancy is considered a temporary disability. This temporary problem gives a service woman the "right to stay in the service or get out," as Mitchell (1989) puts it.

According to the Roper Poll of the Military, "56 percent of those who were deployed in Desert Shield/Desert Storm with mixed gender units reported that women in their unit became pregnant just prior to or while deployed in the Gulf" (Presidential Commission Report, 1993). The report also says that forty-six percent of that group reported that pregnancies had a negative impact on unit readiness, and fifty-nine percent reported a negative impact on morale. These briefings before the Commission showed that women were three times more non-deployable than men, primarily due to pregnancy, during Operation Desert Shield and Desert Storm.

Government statistics also show that women in the U.S. military involved in Desert Shield/Desert Storm were three times more likely to be nondeployable than men. The cumulative report over an eight month period reported that Army women were 3.3 times more nondeployable than men, Navy women 3.7 times, Air Force women 3.5 times, and Marine Corps women 3.9 times more nondeployable than men in Desert Shield/Desert Storm.

The pregnancy rate is causing another problem: single parenthood. In 1989, Mitchell wrote, “11 percent of all servicewomen are single parents and estimations are that more than a third of all pregnant servicewomen are unmarried. Air Force women are six times more likely than Air Force men to be single parents."

What would Theodore Roosevelt think about women in combat units with such high pregnancy rates, low deployability rates, and without having husbands? Theodore Roosevelt did say this, “The woman who, whether from cowardice, from selfishness, from having a false and vacuous ideal shirks her duty as wife and mother, earns the right to our contempt, just as does the man who, from any motive, fears to do his duty in battle when the country calls him” (Adams, 1990).

UNIT COHESION

Are there effects on unit cohesion? This topic includes male bonding, morale, heterosexual sex with members of one's own unit, (known traditionally as fraternization), and the issue of homosexuality and lesbianism. Does an all male heterosexual infantry unit have better unit cohesion, higher unit morale, and in the end, is that unit more effective with a higher level of fighting power?

Introducing women into ground combat units could have an adverse affect on unit cohesion. The fact that women lack the stamina and endurance has already been established. However, introducing women into the equation also introduces other factors that weren't there before.

First, it damages male bonding. This male bonding is a prerequisite to effective fighting power in all ages. Henry V showed what John Keegan calls the theatrical impulse when he rallied his troops before the Battle of Agincourt through his charismatic oratorical skill. The famous phrase, whereby Shakespeare's Henry V captures the essence of male bonding, is the line "We few, we happy few, we band of brothers." Therefore, this argument, more so than all the others, is the most important argument as to why women and homosexuals should not be allowed into American infantry combat units. To do so would break the band of brothers and destroy the male bonding, which is crucial for attaining the highest level of what Van Creveld referred to as fighting power.

Another factor that comes into play when introducing women into combat units is sexual tension, which damages unit cohesion. For example, the United States Navy Ship *Acadia* had a mission to support other United States units involved in Operation Desert Storm in Kuwait and Iraq in 1991. The *Acadia* could not accomplish its mission on time because, with a crew that included 360 females, 36 pregnant crewmembers had to be flown back to shore. The ship became known as the "Love Boat." Ten percent of the females on the ship *Acadia* could no longer perform their duties as sailors. It was even worse on the United States Navy's ship *Yellowstone*, whereby 31 percent of the female crew became pregnant. Putting young women into the mix of young men causes fraternization problems. The young men fight over the young women. The young women end up pregnant. Sex becomes paramount in importance. Defending the country becomes secondary.

Nancy Kassebaum Baker's report on women in the military, which was sponsored by the United States Government, stated that men and women in the military need to be segregated during basic training. The report also concluded that men and women in the military need to be segregated in the barracks or any other living arrangements that are being implemented. The reason Nancy Kassenbaum Baker came to these conclusions was because of the high levels of sexual fraternization she found in the co-ed barracks and the lowering of physical standards she saw in co-ed basic training (Gutmann, 2000).

How can you have unit cohesion on the battlefield when you have segregation in training and in living space? The word cohesion and the word segregation are antonyms not synonyms. Unit cohesion is nearly impossible to achieve when women are put into combat units.

Lesbians have found a home in the United States military. Mitchell (1989) reports:

> In 1980, the USS Norton Sound earned an unhappy reputation as "the ship of Queens" when 24 of 61 women aboard were accused of homosexual activity. In March 1988, the Defense Department revealed that women were three times more likely to be discharged for homosexuality than men.

Homosexuality and bisexuality attempt to blur the line between what is a man and what is a woman. Often times the result is androgyny, which has been characterized by "androgynous Pat" on Saturday Night Live and the co-ed bathroom on Ally McBeal. It has also been displayed on prime time television with Ellen Degeneres' lesbian kiss. The media is pushing hard for this.

Many liberals want to lift the ban on women in combat and in so doing draft women in equal numbers with men. Feminist scholars promote the idea of androgyny and denounce the traditional classical ideals of masculine strength and feminine beauty. Calvin Klein's CK1 for a man or a woman is pro-androgyny. They choose female models that look prepubescent, so that their bodies will still be shaped like those of boys. The model Kate Moss, in what is known as the "heroin chic," exemplifies this look. Feminists promote anorexia in the name of androgyny. Then they cry about its effects, as in the book *Reviving Ophelia*. They refuse to look at the facts put forward by Christina Hoff Sommers in her books *Who Stole Feminism* and *The War on Boys*.

Androgyny's aim is to destroy machismo and destroy classical femininity and replace it with a unisex system. Shakespeare's Lady Macbeth prayed to the devil to "unsex me" so she could become strong like a man, and have "the milk of human kindness" stripped from her breasts, so she could gain the masculine killer instinct. Is that what our culture wants?

> Yet do I fear thy nature. It is too full o'the milk of human kindness. Come you spirits that tend on mortal thoughts, unsex me here, and fill me, from the crown to the toe, topful of direst cruelty! Make thick my blood, stop up the access and passage to remorse, that no compunctions visiting of nature shake my fell purpose, nor keep peace between the effect and it! Come to my woman's breasts, and take my milk for gall, when you durst do it, then you were a man, and to be more than what you were, you

> would be so much more the man. I dare do all that may become a man. Bring forth men-children only, for thy undaunted mettle should compose nothing but males.
>
> I have given suck, and know how tender 'tis to love the babe that milks me. I would, while it was smiling in my face, have plucked my nipple from his boneless gums and dashed the brains out.

Sexual fraternization between members of the same unit will breed chaos, pettiness, mistrust, lack of respect, jealousy and hate. Human nature cannot be stopped. This is why women and homosexuals should not be allowed into American infantry combat units. If those two elements are excluded, then there will definitely be no action or even temptation to have sexual relations with members of one's own unit. Hence, war-fighting capability can be pursued under the Henry V epic of the classical band of brothers. We few, we happy few! We do not include those that Shakespeare's Henry V says, "hold their manhood cheap."

Charles Sasser, a man who has served twenty-four years in the United States military, was called to duty for Operation Desert Storm. Sergeant Sasser said he had to "constantly referee fights between women, half of whom were pregnant, over petty matters." The ten percent of his female company took ninety percent of his problem-solving time. "The female soldiers were continuously bickering and squabbling over issues most men would have found inconsequential. Minor personal grievances flared constantly." Was Shakespeare right, "the lady doth protest too much." What has the United States military come to when Sergeants find themselves spending more time settling "female spats" instead of waging war?

Maybe some of these women in Desert Shield and Desert Storm need to follow Hamlet's advice to Ophelia: "Get thee to a nunn'ry, why wouldst thou be a breeder of sinners." No wonder the nationally syndicated columnist Maureen Dowd was able to write that Georgetown University in Washington, D.C. no longer requires English literature majors to study Shakespeare.

James M. Brantley, a master sergeant, served twenty years in the Air Force and is a Vietnam Veteran. Mr. Brantley is currently an engineering consultant on aircraft safety systems. Sergeant Brantley is against women in combat for many reasons. Brantley believes that women damage unit cohesion, which reduces combat effectiveness. For example, Brantley cites Sergeant Mary Rader who said, "We had females and males that would go to guard duty together and be caught necking, and they're supposed to be out there protecting us and pulling guard duty at 2 and 3 o'clock in the morning. And they had no idea what was going on out there." Rader also said sexual activity in her unit was "very heavy."

Brantley also cited examples of women in combat zones or with combat type jobs who did not rise to the occasion. He said that this anecdotal evidence is a microcosm of a much more prevalent and broad sweeping problem:

> During the 1976 war scare in Korea, some women soldiers requested immediate transfers to the rear. Others showed up in formation carrying babies. During the Panama Invasion, two female truck drivers broke into tears and refused to carry troops into areas where Panamanian snipers were active. The women said they had been driving for eight hours and were afraid they couldn't drive safely because they were tired. They were replaced and never punished. Two other women drivers assigned to a cross-country convoy were refused a request to be excused. One later came under fire and stopped, petrified with fear.

Sergeant Brantley's examples clearly show that women in combat are not a good idea if one's objective is to maintain or increase the United States military's fighting power.

William Shakespeare said in his play *Hamlet*, "Frailty, thy name is woman." We now go to a modern example of a woman who was yearning to be a combat naval aviator. Her name was Kara Hultgreen. *Newsweek*, February 5, 1996 (p.71) had this to say:

> Lt. Kara Hultgreen stuck it out longer. Six feet tall, she was called "the Incredible Hulk." Hultgreen was one of the first women chosen to fly an F-14--the supersonic carrier-based fighter--in a combat squadron. Under normal conditions, she would have washed out. Two "downs"--serious mistakes in training--are usually enough to disqualify a pilot. Hultgreen had four, but she still qualified, in part because the Navy felt tremendous pressure to promote women after Tailhook '91. When Hultgreen crashed and died attempting to land on a carrier in October 1994 on a clear, calm California day, the Navy publicly defended her, claiming she died because of engine failure. The brass tried to suppress a secret report blaming pilot error, which was leaked to the press.

What would Shakespeare think about women in combat? What would Shakespeare think about the physical strength of women? What would Shakespeare think about women who offered war as a way of life? Shakespeare had this to say by way of Katherine's final speech in the *Taming of the Shrew*:

> I am ashamed that women are so simple to offer war where

> they should kneel for peace, or seek for rule, supremacy, and sway, when they are bound to serve, love, and obey. Why are our bodies soft and weak and smooth, Inept to toil and trouble in the world, But that our soft conditions and our hearts should well agree with our external parts? (Shakespeare, 1948, Edited by Harrison)

Shakespeare seems to be opposed to women in combat, and maybe that is one of the reasons why the professors at Georgetown University in Washington D.C. are opposed to Shakespeare.

FOREIGN COUNTRIES

The idea of women in combat units in foreign armies has not been a resounding success. No Israeli women have served in combat since 1948. Viet Cong women served in support roles for the most part during the Vietnam War. "The only all female Viet Cong Company led by a woman had to be inactivated because of defections and desertions" (Brantley, 1993).

In 1989, Canada made it legal for women to serve in Canadian combat units. This decision did not lead to success, but on the contrary, it led to failure on a grand scale. Liberal feminist hopes for equality of outcome did not materialize.

> Of 102 women who volunteered for the Canadian infantry since 1989, only one

> finished the course. She has since left the military. The difference between the Canadian approach and the American approach was that women had to meet the same requirements as men. One Canadian non-commissioned officer said: "A great many women tried to make the infantry...with the exception of only one woman, all others have failed despite repeated recoursing. I have seen women attempting infantry training in Wainwright, attempting both pugil training and self-defense with men. To put it bluntly, they lost every time, all the time, in no time. It was no contest." Women have no place in the infantry or any military occupation, which will require combat conditions involving physical strength. (Brantley, 1993).

The experiences of foreign countries has not confirmed the success of allowing women to serve in combat units. On the contrary, it shows the folly of such actions.

COMPULSORY DRAFT

"Another important consideration is the impact placing women in combat units would have on the legal status of women and a compulsory draft for military service." In *Rostker versus Goldberg*, "the Supreme Court determined that the purpose of the draft was to raise combat soldiers, and because women could not serve in those units, the government could exempt them from registering for the draft" (Presidential Commission Report, 1993).

Presently, women are not in jeopardy of conscription, as long as women are exempt from combat duty. However, if women are placed into combat units, women might become subject to the draft because "the equal protection clause of the Constitution will apply to the military and the courts may have no choice but to mandate it" (Presidential Commission Report, 1993).

If women are legally allowed to serve in the United States military combat units, then the next time the United States has a draft, women will have to be drafted in equal numbers as men, in order to ward off sexual discrimination lawsuits, filed by men who do not want to serve. Do we want our daughters legally obligated to serve in the next Vietnam?

CONCLUSION

In the old brown boot army, the officers said that the infantry was the Queen of Battle and the other combat arms were for its support. The infantry still is the Queen of Battle, and the Queen of Battle is an extremely jealous woman, who can only be served by men.

In the classic treatise on the Korean War, T.R. Fahrenbach wrote that:

> It is time for free, decent societies to continue to control their military forces, but to quit

> demanding from them impossible acquiescence in the liberal view toward life. A 'modern' infantry may ride sky vehicles into combat, fire, and sense its weapons through instrumentation, employ devices of frightening lethality in the future-but it must also be old fashioned enough to be iron-hard, poised for instant obedience, and prepared to die in the mud.
>
> If liberal, decent societies cannot discipline themselves to do all these things, they may have nothing to offer the world. They may not last long enough. (Fahrenbach, 1963)

In conclusion, it is obvious that women should continue to be legally excluded from the combat arms in the United States Military for three major reasons. First, most women lack the upper body strength that is still essential in modern day combat. Second, the nondeployability rate of women in the military far exceeds that of men. Third, unit cohesion is damaged by the introduction of women into combat units. Women in United States military combat units would decrease the units' combat effectiveness, and therefore weaken the defense posture of the United States of America.

Postscript to this story: In 1994, President Bill Clinton had his subordinate, Secretary of Defense Les Aspin, abolish the Department of Defense's "Risk Rule", which stated that women were not to be deployed to forward areas where there is a substantial risk of being captured by enemy forces. No women were to be assigned to combat support units wherein there was a significant risk of capture to those in that unit. This was to prevent our women from being gang raped by foreign enemies of the United States. President Clinton abolished the "Risk Rule" by executive fiat, and it led to the capture and rape of Private Jessica Lynch in the second Gulf War. Because the "Risk Rule" was no longer in effect, Lynch was assigned to a forward combat support unit. Juanita Broderick claimed that she was raped because of the physical actions of Bill Clinton. Jessica Lynch was raped because of the political actions of Bill Clinton. So much for the idea of women in combat being considered a good, positive, humane policy.

5
The Optimistic Environmentalist

"You egomaniacal idiot. You think you can destroy the planet? My what intoxicating power you must have. You can't destroy this planet. You can't even come close."

-Michael Crichton
Jurassic Park

The orthodox Environmentalist view is akin to that of Chicken Little's view, "The sky is falling!" Al Gore wrote a book entitled *Earth in the Balance*, which promoted the environmentalist orthodoxy that capitalist Western Civilization is destroying the planet. In short, environmentalists like Gore say industrialization leads to pollution, which leads to the destruction of our environment. These environmentalists falsify or exaggerate their statistics so that they can raise the level of fear, which in turn raises the level of money they can generate from donors. This allows them to gain more political clout so that they can attack the capitalist system, which they hate. These socialists no longer worship "Our Father that art in Heaven;" they now worship "mother earth." They have exchanged the religion of their ancestors (Christianity or Judaism) for another religion that is more politically correct today. They will fight to defend this religion even if they have to lie.

Al Gore wrote that, "Modern industrial civilization as presently organized, is colliding violently with our planet's ecological system." This view is supported by most of the top ranking left wing scientists and news media elite. Edward O. Wilson, Paul Ehrlich, Green Peace, Lester Brown, *The Scientific American*, CNN, CBS, *The New York Times*, and *Time* all support and perpetuate Gore's thesis that the "earth is in the balance."

Time says, "Everyone knows the planet is in bad shape." In their book *Our Angry Earth*, Isaac Asimov and Frederik Pohl state that, "It is already too late to save our planet from harm."

The main arguments put forth by the left wing environmentalists and the so-called "mainstream" news media are the following: 1. Deforestation-if it continues at its current rate, it will destroy our planet. 2. Extinction-40,000 species become extinct every year. This will eventually destroy our planet. 3. Global Warming-If it continues at its current rate, it will destroy our planet. Their favorite argument in the 1980's was that "acid rain" would destroy our forests and therefore our planet. But for some strange reason, they no longer talk about "acid rain" on the nightly news broadcasts.

Unfortunately for the left wing environmentalists and the liberals in the news media, the facts do not support their claims. I first realized this when I read a book by Bjorn Lomborg entitled *The Skeptical Environmentalist.* It was published in 2001, but I did not find out about it until the *American Spectator* reviewed it in its March/April 2002 Edition. Rush Limbaugh followed this up, when he interviewed Lomborg in his May 2002 edition of *The Limbaugh Letter*. I realized the left was lying once again. Lomborg destroyed their "earth in the balance" thesis with hardcore statistical facts that cannot be denied.

Lomborg states that, "The longest data series from the U.N.'s F.A.O. show that global forest cover has increased from 30.04 percent of the global land area in 1950 to 30.89 percent in 1994, an increase of 0.85 percentage points over the last 44 years." Deforestation is not destroying our planet. Why hasn't the news media communicated these facts to the masses? Why have they delivered the opposite message? Why do the textbooks at school lie to our children?

The next major argument concerns extinction of species. The liberal environmentalists say that humans, especially in Brazil, should not be allowed to cut down trees because cutting trees has led to 40,000 more species going extinct every year. This will eventually destroy our planet, they say.

On page 252 of his book, Lomborg dismantles the dogma that 40,000 species go extinct every year. The *American Spectator* summed it up this way: "Lomborg...challenges the widely accepted figure that 40,000 species go extinct every year. The British scientist Norman Myers first used the number in 1979. Yet what was the evidence for it? Here is what Myers actually said: 'Let us suppose that, as a consequence of this man-handling of the natural environments, the final one-quarter of this century witnesses the elimination of one million species, a far from unlikely prospect. This would work out, during the course of 25 years, at an average rate of 40,000 species per year.' That's it. No data at all-just a circular assumption: If

40,000 species go extinct each year, then 40,000 species go extinct each year." This is circular reasoning based purely on speculation. It is not documentation based on fact. The truth is 40,000 species *do not* go extinct each year.

The I.U.C.N., The World Conservation Union, which maintains the official red list of threatened animals, says that, "actual extinctions remain low." Lomborg states the following on page 255 of his book: "About 86 percent of the Brazilian Amazon rain-forest is still intact. On the other hand, Brazil's Atlantic Rainforest had been almost entirely cleared in the nineteenth century, with only 12 percent left. According to Edward O. Wilson's rule of thumb, one ought to expect half of all the species to have become extinct. However, when members of the Brazilian Society of Zoology analyzed all 171 known Atlantic Forest animals, the group 'could not find a single known animal species which could be properly declared as extinct, in spite of the massive reduction in area and fragmentation of their habitat.' " The environmentalist left wing claims that 10-100 percent of species will go extinct in the next 50 years. Lomborg says the truth is that only 0.7 percent, at the most, will go extinct over the next 50 years. Lomborg bases his number on the "U.N Global Biodiversity Assessment" and a model by biologists Mawdsley and Stork.

The environmentalist left wing seems to make up their numbers out of the thin blue air. Lomborg says the following on page 256, "According to Professor Ehrlich, we do not know just how many species are becoming extinct each year. Yet, 'biologists don't need to know how many species there are, how they are related to one another, or how many disappear annually to recognize that Earth's biota is entering a gigantic spasm of extinction.' This is a most surprising statement. Apparently it alleviates scientists of the need to demonstrate the amount of losses as long as they can feel they are right. Such a statement seems to abandon the ordinarily assumed duty of scientists to objectively gather evidence to help society make real, well-informed choices." The school textbooks promote left wing "scientific" theories as hard scientific facts. Much of their so-called science education is merely political and philosophical indoctrination paraded as "science." The facts are subordinated to the importance of the political or philosophical cause.

What are the implications of liberal environmentalists exaggerating the numbers on the extinction of species? What are their political policy objectives? Lomborg attempts to answer that question on page 257 of his book by saying, "Scientific luminaries such as Harvard biologist E.O. Wilson and Stanford biologist Paul Ehlrich are the enthusiastic supporters of an ambitious plan, the Wildlands Projects, to move the entire population of the United States so as to recreate a natural wilderness in most of the North American continent. The people would then live in small enclosed city islands, as an archipelago surrounded by wilderness and crisscrossed by wildlife corridors." Are these "scientific" tree huggers going to adopt the life style of the Unabomber by living out in the woods in a shack without running water or electricity, or will they continue to indulge in their creature comforts as they bash the society that created their comforts? The difference between these left wing environmentalist scientists and Henry David Thoreau is that Henry David Thoreau practiced what he preached. Thoreau actually lived out in the wilderness for a while on Walden Pond. These charlatans of science remind me of Rousseau, who wrote a book on how to educate the young (*Emile*), while he himself abandoned his own children to the orphanage. That is why they hate Lomborg, because Lomborg exposed them for what they are. Lomborg pointed out that the emperor has no clothes.

Do any other major figures in the environmentalist movement agree with Lomborg? The cofounder of Greenpeace, the most famous environmentalist organization in the world, was Patrick Moore. Moore wrote an article called "Environmentalism for the Twenty-First Century," which was published in 2001 in an anthology entitled *You Are Being Lied To*. In that article the Greenpeace cofounder agreed with Lomborg that present day "environmental extremists" are lying about the number of species that go extinct each year (they greatly exaggerate the numbers) and that they are lying about the statistics on deforestation of the earth, by once again greatly exaggerating the numbers. Moore wrote, "According to the FAO (Food and Agriculture Organization of the United Nations) the area of forests in the industrialized world is actually growing by about 0.2% per year, due to the reforestation of land that was previously cleared for farming." Moore went on to write that, "There is no evidence that a mass extinction is actually occurring now, even though the article [in *National Geographic*, Feb. 1999, entitled, "Biodiversity: The Fragile Web-The Sixth Extinction."] plainly implies that it is."

Patrick Moore, the former president of Greenpeace Canada, believes that much of the environmentalist movement has been hijacked by "environmental extremists" who are more concerned with promoting their left wing political agenda than they are concerned with the welfare of human beings. Patrick Moore wrote that, "Environmental extremists are: anti-human, anti-technology, anti-science, anti-trade, anti-business, and anti-civilization." Patrick Moore, the cofounder of Greenpeace, says that "environmental extremists" want to return to a mythical "utopian" society that is one with nature and bereft of all modern technology. They failed to read Hobbes who accurately told us that, "Life in the state of nature is nasty, brutish, and short."

The next major environmental issue the left wing is exaggerating is global warming. According to former U.S. President Clinton, global warming is "one of the two or three major issues facing the world over the next 30 years."

The left wing environmentalists and their lackeys in the news media like to blame global warming on Western Civilization. They never blame it on Mother Nature. That is why they have tried to suppress Nigel Calder's book, *The Manic Sun* (1997), which blamed the sun for increasing global temperatures.

Lomborg says that, "temperatures have increased 0.6 degrees Celsius over the past century" but that this is not a dramatic divergence from previous centuries. Lomborg states that global warming's negative effects have been exaggerated. "Global warming will not decrease food production, it will probably not increase storminess or the frequency of hurricanes, it will not increase the impact of malaria or indeed cause more deaths. It is even unlikely that it will cause more flood victims, because a much richer world will protect itself better."

Lomborg says that the news media discusses global warming "with a fervor more fitting for preachers of opposing religions." Lomborg hit the nail on the head. This worship of mother earth and the celebration of Earth Day (invented in 1970) are more important to them than Christmas or Easter. Mother Earth is a god in their pagan pantheon, alongside Marx, Darwin, and Freud. To point out any flaws in the theories of any of these men is to go against their naturalistic religion. It is a clash of worldviews.

Lomborg writes on page 319, " The discussion of global warming is not just a question of choosing the optimal economic path for humanity, but it has much deeper, political roots as to what kind of future society we would like." Lomborg reveals the environmentalists' goals and motives on page 320. "What the IPCC suggests-and openly admits-is that we need to change individual lifestyles, and move away from consumption. We must focus on sharing resources." Once again the Marxist motive of doing away with capitalistic consumption and doing away with private ownership of property and wealth comes to the fore. These left wing environmentalists want women to have the choice to kill their unborn children, but not have the choice to drive an S.U.V. These left wing environmentalists massage the numbers, so that they can build a socialist utopia where we all share our wealth collectively and live together singing John Lennon's "Imagine." These leftists still believe in the Marxist ideology of socialism long after the fall of the Berlin Wall and the demise of the Soviet Union. They don't let the facts confuse them.

Is the media biased in its reporting of "scientific" news? Lomborg says the following on page 322: "In the reporting from the major media, such as CNN, CBS, the Times, and Time, it was found that all used the high estimate of 5.8 degrees Celsius warming, and yet none mentioned the low estimate of 1.4 degrees Celsius." Both numbers were in the scientific source. The report gave a range. The media refused to reveal the truth of this range and ran with only the extreme high-end number. This was an official United Nations report on Global Warming that was putting forth estimates of the rise in temperatures by 2100. And the liberals say there is no bias in the media. They say that only to deceive the public and preserve their credibility. But the truth will win out in the end and the media moguls will be exposed for the liars that they are.

How have the left wing scientists responded to Lomborg's good news that the earth is in better shape then we thought and that we are not destroying our planet? Instead of rejoicing at the good news, they are fighting mad and have attacked Lomborg viciously. They literally threw a pie in his face. Lomborg told Limbaugh that "when your opponents throw a pie in your face you know that they have run out of arguments." E.O. Wilson called Lomborg a "parasite." Limbaugh said the *Scientific American* ran a series of articles whose sole purpose was to trash Lomborg. The *American Spectator's* Matt Ridley wrote that, "The Editor of *Scientific American,* condemns Lomborg for his 'presumption' in challenging 'investigators who have devoted their lives' to the subject, as if seniority defined truth." Remember Jesus Christ had more knowledge and wisdom at age 12 then all the learned scholars in the Temple.

These leftists hate Lomborg even more than they hate Rush Limbaugh. This is because Limbaugh was always a conservative, but Lomborg was a left wing member of Green Peace, and is still a vegetarian who does not own a car. Myers, the man who purports to know that 40,000 species go extinct every year, accepts prize money from Volvo, an automobile manufacturer. Who is the real honest environmentalist? Lomborg or Myers? These leftists see Lomborg as a traitor to their cause. *Rolling Stone* said Lomborg has greater credibility on their issue, because he is a leftist politically and a no-car owning vegetarian. This is why the leftists hate Lomborg more than Limbaugh. They consider Lomborg an apostate, a heretic, one who must be excommunicated from the environmentalist church. Limbaugh had never been a member of that particular denomination.

One of the greatest radio commentators of our era, Rush Limbaugh, summed it up beautifully when he wrote the following advice in the *Limbaugh Letter*, May 2000 edition, " *The Skeptical Environmentalist* by Bjorn Lomborg is a book, my friends, that every one of you should study. And give it to your kids-to counter the environmental nonsense they get in school, they'll need this powerful ammo. Learn it, love it, live it." Thank you; Rush, for your honesty and eloquence. No one could say it better.

6
Einstein v. Bohr on Quantum Physics

"God does not play dice."

-Albert Einstein challenging Bohr's interpretation of Quantum Physics

Is there an objective reality? Is there an objective truth? Intellectuals used to believe in objective reality. Intellectuals used to believe in one objective truth. This all changed when Neils Bohr supposedly defeated Albert Einstein in a series of quantum physics debates in Copenhagen in 1927 and 1930. Neil's Bohr stated emphatically that quantum physics called for "a radical revision of our attitude toward the problem of physical reality."

The debate over the proper way to interpret quantum physics, which pitted Einstein versus Bohr, is absolutely fascinating and is of the utmost importance even to the present day. What was the debate? What were the issues? Who were the players? Why does it matter? I shall attempt to answer these questions.

Most physicists today are disciples of Bohr and Heisenberg. They are indeterminists and subjectivists. They believe in Bohr's complementarity and Heisenberg's uncertainty principle. They believe everything is random and based on statistical probabilities. They believe that there is no reality unless and until it is observed. They believe that there is no reality independent of the observer. They are the liberals of modern physics and they control most of the physics departments in our educational institutions. They are known collectively as the "Copenhagen School" of quantum physics.

A minority of physicists today are intellectual protégés of Albert Einstein. Einstein and his followers are determinists and objectivists. They do not believe in Bohr's complementarity. They do not believe in Heisenberg's uncertainty principle. Instead they believe in objective reality independent of the observer. They believe there is only one reality. One truth. This group of physicists includes Einstein, Schrodinger, Planck, and Carver Mead.

The academic orthodoxy in theoretical physics for the last seventy years is that Bohr was right and Einstein was wrong. This false orthodoxy was pushed in the textbooks for political and philosophical purposes. The truth was suppressed. Any new scientific evidence that undermined Bohr and strengthened Einstein's interpretation was swept under the rug. It was not printed in the textbooks. The promoters of subjectivity and uncertainty were 100% certain that they were right.

Left wing philosophers helped to shape this modern school of thought championed by Bohr and Heisenberg. On page 120 of his book *Einstein versus Bohr*, Sachs writes, "Heisenberg's positivistic attitude in his physics reflected Machs philosophy, as well as that of the 'Vienna Circle', a philosophical group of the early part of the twentieth century that had an important influence on physics."

Einstein said, "I reject the basic idea of contemporary statistical quantum theory."

Schrodinger attacked Bohr's complementarity as "intellectually wicked." Murray Gell-Mann accused Bohr of "brainwashing" the majority of physicists. (Murray Gell-Mann was a Nobel Prize winner in physics.)

What was "intellectually wicked" about Bohr's lack of belief in an objective physical reality? Part of it was that he did not want this belief confined to the field of physics. He wanted to spread this virulent strain of ideology to dominate all fields of human inquiry and knowledge, not just science. "Bohr regarded complementarity as providing an 'epistemological lesson' for the whole field of human learning, and beyond physics his own discussions were principally in biology, psychology, and social anthropology." In 1939, Bohr preached cultural subjectivity (that all cultures are equal) and moral subjectivity (that no moral decision is inferior to any other moral decision). For instance, a cannibalistic culture is not inferior to a culture that does not practice cannibalism. Bohr said, "each culture represents a harmonious balance of traditional conventions by means of which latent potentialities of human life can unfold themselves in a way which reveals to us new aspects of its unlimited richness and variety."

John Bell rebelled against the Bohrian orthodoxy. He spoke out against suppression of information in the textbooks. "Why is the pilot wave picture ignored in textbooks? To show us that vagueness, subjectivity, and indeterminism are not forced on us by experimented facts, but by deliberate theoretical choice?"

Selleri says that the Copenhagen paradigm of Bohr and Heisenberg contains a "falsification." Selleri goes on to say that there is an objective reality in spite of the falsification put forth so effectively by the Copenhagen clan.

Einstein may have lost the debate in the short term, but Einstein will be proven the victor in the long run. Carver Mead proved that Einstein was right and that it was Bohr who was wrong about quantum physics. Mead proved this in his book *Collective Electrodynamics*, which was published in 2001.

Carver Mead is the greatest living physicist, not just in theory but also in practice. Silicon Valley knows him as the most "influential physicist of the microelectronics revolution." Our computer speed is dependent upon his inventions. He won the 1999 MIT prize for invention and innovation. He is the inventor of the Foveon Camera. According to Rich Karlgaard of Forbes, "Carver has invented color processing chips that do for color photography and video what Dolby did for sound." Mead's new book overturns the left wing Bohrian orthodox interpretation of quantum physics.

Rich Karlgaard states in *Forbes* on March 18, 2002, in a review of Carver Mead's book, "Einstein had objected to Werner Heisenberg's uncertainty principle and, in general, to the statistics-based, ultimately random foundation of life Bohr was promoting. 'God does not play dice' with the universe, Einstein protested. Carver Mead said that Bohr's signature contribution to physics, complementarity, is crap. There is only one reality. The supposed conflicts of Bohr's day were a result of limited instrumentation. But instead of being patient, Bohr forced the issue and declared all problems solved. He silenced two generations of physicists. Carver loathes Bohr's legacy. He thinks Bohr perpetrated one of those monstrous intellectual frauds that every now and then slips through the asylum gates and confuses people for decades. Think Freud and Marx."

Carver Mead is a Renaissance man, in an age of specialists. Carver Mead, unlike most physicists, sees the whole forest, not just one or two individual trees. Like Leonardo Da Vinci and Ben Franklin, he is an inventor, scientist, artist, and philosopher all rolled into one. Mead understands that all knowledge is interrelated. Mead says, "The creative process starts with the juxtaposition of two concepts from separate conceptual spaces." This is like the Wright Brothers taking an automobile engine and using it to invent the airplane. Carver Mead warns us that too much specialization and fragmentation of knowledge in academia leads to the destruction of our ability to innovate. Specializing within one box does not allow one to think outside that box. That is why the Renaissance man genius must read widely on his own.

As military planners used to say, "KISS-Keep It Simple, Stupid." The simpler the plan, the less likely it will be messed up. Carver Mead says that the only hope for one man to master the ever-expanding body of knowledge is through the "unification and simplification of the knowledge base." Mead says that to give up on trying to be a well-read Renaissance man and specialize in only one small area is a defeatist attitude and a cop-out.

Carver Mead lists ten experimental discoveries which vindicate Einstein and debunk Bohr's interpretation of quantum physics: 1933-Persistent current in superconducting ring, 1933-Expulsion of magnetic field by superconductor, 1954-Maser, 1960-Atomic Laser, 1961-Quantized flux in superconducting ring, 1962-semiconductor laser, 1964-superconducting quantum interference device, 1980-integer quantum hall effect, 1981-fractional quantum hall effect, 1996-Bose-Einstein condensate.

Bohr was able to seem as if he defeated Einstein in the Copenhagen Debates of 1927 and 1930 because they were prior to these new discoveries. Another reason many believed Bohr won the debates was because "the equipment for the experiments was crude by today's standards." New equipment, new technologies, and new discoveries vindicate Einstein and prove that Bohr's Copenhagen claim was in error.

I recently asked a prominent high school physics teacher if he had heard of Carver Mead. He answered, "No." The textbooks and the teachers of physics are not even aware of the truth. This new information is being suppressed. The news media and textbook publishers are suppressing this information for political and philosophical reasons. They believe admitting that physics has proven objective reality would help give more credibility to conservative Christians and conservative Jews who believe in an objective reality, and the ideas of moral and cultural objectivity that flow from that. This they want to avoid at all costs. If they do not suppress the truth, the charade of political correctness will suffer a devastating blow.

Objective reality based on one universal truth means that some cultural practices are superior to other cultural practices and that some moral decisions are superior to other moral decisions. For example, Judeo-Christian Western Civilization is superior to the pagan civilizations found in the third world, and sexual intercourse between man and wife is morally superior to sodomy between two men. These beliefs are totally unacceptable to the modern liberal world-view.

The modern liberals cling to two pillars of thought: cultural subjectivity (also called multiculturalism), and moral subjectivity (sometimes called moral relativism). Cultural subjectivity states that all cultures are equal. Moral subjectivity states that all moral decisions are equal. The decision to abort a baby, according to this theory, is morally equal to the decision to give birth to a baby. The modern liberals use Bohr's majority view on quantum physics to support their left wing ideology. That is why they suppress the truth about quantum physics from the textbooks. If the truth were widely known, Bohr's Copenhagen paradigm would collapse and the intellectual "scientific" support for the liberal subjective view of life would also collapse. When you take out the foundation of a structure, the upper floors will also fall. This is what they are trying to prevent.

Einstein knew that the quantum physics emperor had no clothes. Einstein blew the whistle on Bohr. Bohr verbally lambasted Einstein and sent him into exile for the latter part of his life. Einstein lived from then on as a recluse. The Copenhagen Clan and the majority of physicists dismissed Einstein and his views on quantum physics as ridiculous. They thought Einstein was now a senile old fool. He didn't go with the new flow; he didn't change with the times. Einstein was like King Lear after he was betrayed by two of his ungrateful daughters. Bohr and Heisenberg should have shown more deference and respect to their king instead of banishing him into exile. The truth is Einstein understood all too well, and that is why he said, "God does not play dice." The certainty of God and His natural law does not co-exist well with the uncertainty of Bohr/Heisenberg. One of them must be wrong.

New technology and instrumentation proves that Einstein was right and that Bohr and Heisenberg were wrong. Tony Siegman said, "Lasers are best defined not as a 'photon process' but as a coherent wave process." Carver Mead says that, "Jaynes, Barut, and Zeh have put us in a position to finally settle the Einstein-Bohr debate-with a resounding victory for Einstein."

Einstein said some politically incorrect things that have been suppressed by the high school physics textbook writers. Einstein said that, "There is only one reality to be described." Many prominent physicists today who follow in Bohr's flawed footsteps believe in multiple universes and multiple realities. They believe that there are parallel universes. One universe where you get up in the morning and brush your teeth and another one in which you get up in the morning and don't brush your teeth. All of this supposedly happens at the same time. They try to hide this from the masses, because they don't want people to think they are crazy.

In 1909, Einstein put forth the following statement: "The elementary process of radiation seems to be directed." This is anathema to the liberal ideology of randomness and chance accounting for all life and life forces. Naturalistic philosophy and Carl Sagan's secular humanism do not allow for God to direct anything. Nothing is directed: it is supposed to be left up to statistical probability and the randomness of meaningless chance.

In the orthodox Darwinian science magazine entitled *Discover*, June 2002 edition, quantum physicist John A. Wheeler promotes the idea that nothing exists unless it is observed. When it is not being observed it does not exist. This shows the lunacy of many modern left wing physicists who have been brainwashed by Bohr's complementarity and Heisenberg's uncertainty. It is still the majority view in academia today, in spite of the truth.

Many scientists hold fast to theories even when there is proof that they are badly flawed. They just put a little band-aid on it when it really needs to be thrown out. Carver Mead in an *American Spectator* interview (September/October, 2001) said, "Ptolemaic astronomers assumed that the earth was at the center. But then it became more and more complex to calculate the orbits of visible planets. When you assume the earth is the center, you have to add epicycles to the existing orbits to adjust them. In the same way, when you assume photons are point particles, and all you can calculate is probability, you have to add epicycles of conceptual nonsense to 'explain' even the simplest experiment."

"If you take today's standard theory of particle physics, and the standard theory of gravitation, it is well known that the result is off by a factor of maybe ten to the power of 50. That's 10 followed by 49 zeroes. And that discrepancy comes from assuming that matter is made up of point particles."

"The theory has to be adjusted, with band aids stuck on top of one another. This happens all the time with science, but especially with the statistical quantum theory."

This same phenomenon of Ptolemaic epicycles is being used in the field of Darwinian Macro-Evolutionary Theory. The leading Darwinian Evolutionist at Harvard University was the late paleontologist Stephen Jay Gould. Mr. Gould was researching the fossil record and realized that it did not fit with Darwinian Evolutionary theory. Darwin had predicted that the fossil record would show lots of intermediate forms spread out evenly throughout the layers of rock. But Gould realized that the reality was much different. What paleontologists found was the "Cambrian Explosion." All the major animal groups show up in the fossil record all at once and fully formed. When Gould realized that this contradicts Darwin, he did not choose to throw out Darwin's theory and start over with a fresh perspective. Instead he chose to put a small band-aid on Darwin's theory. He called it "punctuated equilibrium." It stated that macroevolution happened rapidly in some periods and then plateaus for many years, during which there is not much change at all within a species. It happens in fits and starts. The phrase "Cambrian explosion" has been suppressed from most high school biology texts because it contradicts Darwin's view that evolution can only proceed gradually over long periods of time. Those textbooks that do mention it fail to adequately explain its significance.

Putting a band-aid on a corpse will not bring it back to life in a world where the truth is widely circulated. That is why we need to bypass the liars who are suppressing the truth and get the word out through our own channels of communication. This book is a step in that direction.

Let us never forget what Einstein said: "Concepts which have proved useful for ordering things, easily assume so great an authority over us, that we forget their terrestrial origin and accept them as unalterable facts...the road of scientific progress is frequently blocked for long periods by such errors." Let us not be blinded by the authority of Marx, Freud, Bohr, and Darwin, because they may very well have been in error.

7
The Sphinx and Geology

"Great scientific theories do not usually conquer the world through being accepted by opponents who, gradually convinced of their truth, have finally adopted them. It is always rare to find a Saul becoming a Paul. What happens is that the opponents of the new idea finally die off and the following generation grows up under its influence."
-Max Planck (Nobel Prize winner in Physics)

The orthodox view of the Egyptologists is that the Sphinx in Egypt was built in 2,500 B.C. This would make the Sphinx approximately 4,500 years old. This orthodox view is supported by very little evidence, all of which is circumstantial and highly suspect.

The date for the Sphinx was first put forward by Selim Hassan in 1949. He admitted in his published finding that his evidence was purely circumstantial. In 1860, a statue of Khafre was recovered from the Valley Temple. The Egyptologists said that Khafre's statue proves that Khafre (who reigned in 2,500 B.C.) must have built the Sphinx. The new kingdom Stela found between the paws of the Sphinx contained an inscription, which included the first syllable of Khafre's name. The Egyptologists claim this proves that Khafre built the Sphinx. Egyptologists also argue that Khafres' face looks similar to the face on the Sphinx. Therefore, Khafre must have built it.

The problem with these arguments is that they violate the laws of logical reasoning. The statue of Khafre could just as easily have been put there at a later date. It proves nothing. It was in no way attached to the Sphinx. The first syllable of Khafre's name in hieroglyphics also is the first letter in many other Ancient Egyptian words. That proves nothing. The face of the Sphinx is badly damaged and many say it doesn't look like Khafre. The face of the Sphinx in its modern condition is not precise enough to look like any one particular person. That opinion is not proof.

Recently, new scientific evidence has been put forth that overturns the Orthodox view concerning the date of construction of the Sphinx. Left wing academics and world history textbook publishers are suppressing this new scientific evidence. You cannot read about this in public high school world history textbooks.

What is this new evidence? First, John Anthony West's research based upon the weathering of the Sphinx and climatology in the region led him to the conclusion that the Sphinx was built sometime around 10,000 B.C.

Also, Dr. Robert Schoch, a professor of Geology at Boston University, studied the "precipitation induced weathering" on the Sphinx and came to the conclusion that it had to have been built at least 5,000-7,000 B.C. at a bare minimum. That was the last time there was heavy rainfall in Egypt on a consistent basis. Dr. Schoch presented his findings to the Geological Society of America and 300 American geologists endorsed his conclusion.

The Egyptologists and left wing social scientists went apoplectic. They became filled with rage and anger. They felt humiliated by an outsider who was not an Egyptologist, historian, or political scientist. A geologist named Robert Schoch had pointed out that the Emperor had no clothes. Dr. Schoch had shocked their world. He had pulverized their paradigm and tanked their theory. For psychological, political, and philosophical reasons, the Egyptologists have not admitted that they were wrong. Instead they cling to their orthodoxy and attack anyone who denies the absolute truth of their theory. Therefore, they have attacked Dr. Schoch with insults, and they refuse to embrace him with compliments.

Why do the left wing Egyptologists cling so tenaciously to their orthodoxy even after it has proven to be false? Egyptologist Mark Lehner told the *New York Times* that, "People during that time (5,000-10,500 B.C.) were hunters and gatherers. They didn't build cities." Carol Redmont of the University of California, Berkely, made a similar statement to the *L.A. Times*: "There's just no way that could be true [that the oldest portion of the Sphinx dates back to 5,000 B.C. or earlier]...The people of that region would not have had the technology, the governing institution, or even the will to build such a structure thousands of years before Khafre's reign...[It] flies in the face of everything we know about Ancient Egypt." Dr. Schoch replied, "Does it really? Or does it merely undermine our assumptions? Were the people of long ago unlettered knuckle-draggers who didn't know what a Sphinx was, much less how to build such a massive example of one? Or have we, in the assumed superiority of our own culture, arrogantly written off an ancient, vanished people different from ourselves yet sophisticated in ways we do not understand?"

Graham Hancock says, "Since then, most often out of the public eye, an acrimonious dispute had begun to smoulder between the geologists and the Egyptologists. And though very few people other than John West were prepared to say as much, what was at stake in this dispute was a complete upheaval in accepted views about the evolution of human civilization."

Hancock asked West why the Egyptologists and archeologists are so unwilling to consider the idea that the Sphinx was built in 10,450 B.C. and West replied, "The reason, I think is that they're quite fixed in their ideas about the linear evolution of civilization."

John Anthony West put it quite bluntly in his book *Serpent In The Sky*, "Meanwhile Darwin's Theory of Evolution had been published. When Egyptology began, most scholars, as dutiful sons of the Enlightenment, were atheists, materialists, or only nominally religious. Most were convinced they represented an apogee of civilization. But the process was not yet regarded as inevitable and automatic; the most renowned intellects of the time did not yet regard themselves as advanced apes. It was not yet heretical to suggest that ancient people had actually known something. But as the theory of Evolution became dogma, it became, and remains, impossible to attribute exact knowledge to ancient cultures without undermining the faith in progress" (or without undermining faith in Darwin).

That is the crux of the debate. If we accept the facts we would have to undermine Darwin.

Darwin is a god in the left wing pantheon of ideology. The leftists will defend him at all costs and they will suppress any scientific evidence that undermines his might.

Left wing liberals in academia and the media are suppressing two crucial facts concerning Albert Einstein. The first is that he won the debate against Neils Bohr on quantum physics (which I dealt with in my chapter entitled "Einstein versus Bohr"), and the second fact is that Einstein endorsed Professor Charles Hapgood's "Earth Crust Displacement" theory. Evidence for earth crust displacement, like evidence for the older dating of the Sphinx, disrupts the orthodox, Darwinian, evolutionary timeline. That is why it is so ardently suppressed.

In 1915, Wegener was the first man to propose the "Plate-Tectonic" theory (also known as "Continental Drift" theory). Wegener was viciously attacked at the time, because his theory went against the prevailing paradigm. For 50 years the top academic scientists in the world dismissed Wegener's "Plate Tectonics" theory. Eventually, the scientific community had a 180-degree change of mind and now practically all the textbooks promote plate tectonics theory as a fact of life. The theory simply acknowledges that the Earth's crust is composed of plates that move gradually over time. The old paradigm, which stated that the earth's crust was stationary and could not move any great distances, was overturned. The arrogant scientists had to admit once again that they had been wrong.

However, another theory concerning the movement of the Earth's crust was proposed by professor Charles Hapgood in 1958. It was called Earth Crust Displacement. Hapgood explained his theory in the book *Earth's Shifting Crust: A Key to Some Basic Problems of Earth Science.* Hapgood's extensive research of the evidence led him to the conclusion that the Earth's crust can, and has in the past, shifted all at once in a short period of time, in one piece on top of the semi-liquid layer beneath the Earth's crust known as the asthenosphere. This theory perfectly explained "ice ages" that came and went rapidly on different areas of the Earth's surface.

In 1953, Hapgood asked Albert Einstein to investigate his findings and give him an honest critique of his theory. Einstein reviewed Hapgood's research and conclusions, and Einstein agreed with Hapgood. Einstein endorsed Hapgood's Earth Crust Displacement theory. Einstein wrote the following concerning the buildup of ice on the polar ice caps of the Earth's surface, "The Earth's rotation acts on these unsymmetrically deposited masses, and produces centrifugal momentum that is transmitted to the rigid crust of the Earth. The constantly increasing centrifugal momentum produced this way will, when it reaches a certain point, produce a movement of the earth's crust over the earth's body, and this will displace the polar regions towards the equator." This phenomenon explains why woolly mammoths were found frozen to death in Siberia, Russia with buttercups and warm weather vegetation in their mouths and stomachs (See the Berezovka Mammoth discovered in 1901.).

Einstein enthusiastically supported Hapgood's thesis. Einstein wrote in the forward to Hapgood's book, *The Earth's Shifting Crust*, "I frequently receive communications from people who wish to consult me concerning their unpublished ideas. It goes without saying that these ideas are very seldom possessed of scientific validity. The very first communication, however, that I received from Mr. Hapgood electrified me. His idea is original, of great simplicity, and ...of great importance to everything that is related to the history of the earth's surface." Einstein wrote to Hapgood and said, "I find your arguments very impressive and have the impression that your hypothesis is correct. One can hardly doubt that significant shifts of the crust of the earth have taken place repeatedly and within a short time."

Hapgood's Earth Crust Displacement theory, supported by Einstein, has been completely ignored, dismissed, and suppressed by the left wing academics and their lackeys in the news media. Why have they dismissed Hapgood's theory out of hand? They dismiss it, because in order to accept it, one must accept catastrophism. The orthodox view of geologists is based upon the love of Lyell's and Darwin's gradualism (known as uniformitarianism) and a hatred for catastrophism, which states that changes on the Earth can happen rapidly through cataclysmic floods, earthquakes, volcanic eruptions and the like. Why must geologists, and for that matter almost all of academia and the media, subscribe dogmatically to uniformitarianism (gradual change) as opposed to catastrophism (rapid change)? Because to subscribe to catastrophism, in their minds, is to give scientific legitimacy to the Bible and its catastrophic flood. The secular-humanist, naturalist, atheistic left which controls the dogmatically pro-Darwin National Academy of Sciences will not allow any evidence in the textbooks which might possibly, in any way, shape or form, lend credence to the *Bible.* Their religion of naturalistic science does not allow for catastrophism, because catastrophism happens to be found in the Bible. It is merely a liberal knee jerk reaction for them to extend this to bigotry against conservative Christians, and a prejudice against any catastrophic interpretation of geology, regardless of the facts.

Their naturalist god Charles Darwin wrote that all these biological changes must take place gradually over long periods of time. "Natural Selection can act only by taking advantage of slight successive variations; she can never take a leap, but must advance by the shortest and slowest steps." (Charles Darwin-*On the Origin of Species...* Ch 6, p. 194.). Thinking along the same lines as Darwin, Lyell wrote that all natural geological changes on the face of the earth can only take place gradually over long periods of time (Uniformitarianism). Many modern left wing professors who call themselves objective scientists even attacked their friend and evolution supporter, the late Stephen Jay Gould for proposing "punctuated equilibrium," which strayed from the orthodox Darwinian/Lyellian faith of gradualism. Their liberal knee-jerk reactions are quite predictable.

A liberal pro- Darwin magazine entitled *The Skeptical Inquirer: The Magazine for Science and*

Reason, dated July/August 2002, attacked Professor Charles Hapgood and his theory of Earth Crust Displacement. Why, after all these years of ignoring his theory, is it now being attacked? Because Graham Hancock brought the theory back from the dustbin of history by promoting it in his best seller *The Fingerprints of the Gods*. The Darwinians are now afraid of the positive publicity that Hapgood is getting after years of being suppressed by "mainstream" science.

The most fascinating fact about the article in the *Skeptical Inquirer*, which makes a lame attempt to debunk Professor Hapgood, is not what it says but what it omits. It suppresses the fact that Albert Einstein endorsed Hapgood's theory. The left wing scientists know that this endorsement potentially gives Hapgood instant credibility with the masses, and therefore they suppress it, because their goal is not the truth; their goal is political correctness. In their skewed minds, admitting that Hapgood was correct is tantamount to admitting that the Bible is correct. They fear that accepting catastrophism puts them on a slippery slope that will force them to accept the Biblical flood of Noah. They do not want to renounce their Lyellian-Darwinian religion and accept Jesus Christ as their Lord and Savior. They feel that the stakes in the catstrophism versus uniformitarianism game are extremely high indeed.

This evidence destroys the orthodox macro-evolutionary timeline. That is why Dawkins' left wing atheist allies are suppressing the information. Darwin's Theory allows Mr.

Dawkins, in his own words, "for the first time to be an intellectually fulfilled atheist." Without Darwin's Theory his worldview would collapse. He would no longer be fulfilled. That is what is at stake - the survival of the dominant left wing world-view. The left wing would be hard pressed to survive the destruction of Marx, Freud, and Darwin in such a short period of time.

8
Darwinian Evolution

"In China we can criticize Darwin but not the government. In America you can criticize the government but not Darwin."
Jy Chen-Chinese Paleontologist

The high school and collegiate biology and history textbooks suppress the truth concerning Darwinian Evolutionary Theory. This suppression of factual information is aided and abetted by the liberals who dominate the so-called "mainstream" news media.

Darwin's Racism

The first thing these textbooks suppress are the racist writings and racist views of Charles Darwin. Most of these textbooks never mention the full title of Darwin's most famous book; only the shorter non-racist part of the title is mentioned. The textbooks say Darwin's book in which he advanced his Evolutionary Theory is *The Origin of Species.* That is not the full title. The full title is suppressed because it is racist and if it were revealed it would damage Darwin's credibility. The full title is *On the Origin of Species by Means of Natural Selection or the Preservation of Favoured Races in the Struggle for Life.* Are students in school not entitled to know the full title of Darwin's book? It is a long title, but it should be mentioned the first time the book is mentioned and thereafter be shortened to *Origin of Species.* That is the standard policy used by textbook writers with almost any other long book title. But why with Darwin only do they censor his subtitle every single time; even when the book is first mentioned? It is because they want Darwin's atheism but not his racism. The students are not allowed to learn the whole truth. The left suppresses this factual information. The left wing god Charles Darwin must be protected at all costs, even at the cost of textbooks lying to the children, as the news media lie to the children's parents. The lies of omission are often times more powerful than the lies of commission. What is left out is often more important than what is put in.

When confronted with this evidence, some might say that Darwin was not a racist and that his title was referring to animals and not human beings. But what they fail to realize is that other evidence concerning Darwin's racism is also suppressed from the textbooks. This includes racist writings by Darwin in his book *The Descent of Man* and in his personal letters to colleagues.

In *The Descent of Man*, Darwin wrote, "At some future period, not very distant as measured by centuries, the civilized races of man will almost certainly exterminate, and replace, the savage races throughout the world." Darwin does not say the races of animals; he says explicitly the races of man. Of course this information is suppressed from almost all high school and collegiate biology and history textbooks. The liberals can't allow this quotation to get out, because it would damage the credibility of one of their most sacred theoreticians, the founder of macroevolutionary theory.

On July 3, 1881, Charles Darwin wrote a letter to W. Graham (*Life and Letters of Charles*

Darwin, volume 1, 316, cited in Gertrude Himmelfarb, *Darwin and the Darwinian Revolution*, 1959, p. 343). In it Darwin said the following, "The more civilized so-called Caucasian races have beaten the Turkish hollow in the *Struggle* for existence. Looking to the world at no very distant date, what an endless number of the lower races will have been eliminated by the higher civilized races throughout the world." These quotations have been suppressed by the textbook writers and publishers as well as by the liberals in the news media.

Darwin's friend and supporter, who is featured prominently in a positive light, reinforcing Darwin's evolutionary views, in high school and collegiate biology textbooks, is Ernst Haeckel. Ernst Haeckel served Adolf Hitler. Adolf Hitler loved Darwin's writings. In fact, Hitler borrowed his title for *Mein Kampf*, which in English means *My Struggle*, from Darwin's subtitle *The Preservation of Favoured Races in the Struggle for Life.*

Adolf Hitler tried to take Darwin's theory and put it into practice. Hitler believed his policies were merely speeding up natural Darwinian evolutionary forces. Hitler believed that his euthanasia policies, the killing off of the handicapped and mentally retarded, as well as his policies of "eliminating" what he deemed to be "lower races," would help to "preserve the favoured races in the struggle for life."

Karl Marx and Joseph Stalin were both greatly influenced by the writings of Darwin. Joseph Stalin, who murdered even more people than Adolf Hitler, started out as a theology student. But Darwin impacted his life with greater force than the Bible. Darwin transformed Stalin as a young man (long before he was in power) from a believer in God to a hard-core atheist. This allowed Stalin later to murder millions, because in his view there is no God and therefore there can be no morality. (Nietzsche held the same view, i.e., "God is dead.") The book *Landmarks in the Life of Stalin* by Emelian Yaroslavsky, documents a conversation between Stalin and one of his ecclesiastical school classmates, wherein Stalin says, "I'll lend you a book to read; it will show you that the world and all living things are quite different from what you imagine, and all this talk about God is sheer nonsense." His classmate said, "What book is that?" Stalin replied, "Darwin. You must read it."

Karl Marx, the founder of Communist theory, asked Darwin's permission to dedicate his Communist book *Das Kapital* to Darwin himself. Such has been the influence of Darwin's deception. Unfortunately, all of this information has been suppressed from public high school and collegiate biology and history textbooks.

The same belief system that inspired two of the most prolific mass murderers of the twentieth century, Hitler and Stalin, is the same belief system that is taught in today's classrooms to our school children. It is the same belief system that inspired a totalitarian system, Communism, which enslaved millions over an eighty-year period. Not only is this belief system presented to our school children, it is presented as fact without any challenging viewpoint; all scientific evidence that contradicts macroevolution is censored out of the text. The most disturbing part is the way textbook writers lie and mislead students in presenting Darwinian macroevolution.

Flaws in Darwin's Theory

The evidence put forth in favor of Darwinian macroevolution in high school and collegiate biology textbooks contains both lies of commission as well as lies of omission. The left wing liberal textbook writers lie in order to support a flawed theory. These textbook writers lie by what they put into the book and lie by what they leave out of the book. They try to make Darwin's theory appear to the students to be 100% infallible, inalterable, inerrant fact. Their whole worldview depends upon this brainwashing of our young in the schools. They believe that any scientific evidence that does not support Darwin's Theory should be suppressed at all costs.

Jonathan Wells, who holds a Ph.D. in molecular and cell biology from U.C.-Berkeley, wrote a brilliant book entitled *Icons of Evolution Science or Myth? Why Much of What We Teach About Evolution is Wrong.* Regnery published the book in the year 2000. Every conservative in the United States of America should buy a copy of Wells' book. In this book, Wells illustrates the lies and misleading evidence, which are in almost all of our public high school and collegiate biology texts.

Two of Wells' "icons" deal with blatant cases of academic fraud in the perpetuation of Darwinian theory. The first of these concerns Haeckel's embryos. Ernst Haeckel drew pictures of embryos, which are reproduced in most biology textbooks as evidence for Darwin's theory of evolution. The textbooks fail to mention the following facts. Haeckel was tried for academic fraud at the University of Jena and was convicted. Haeckel faked his drawings in order to help along Darwin's theory. Haeckel also deceived the public by starting his embryo drawings in the middle stages of development instead of at the first few stages, where they look very different. Stephen Jay Gould was Harvard's leading paleontologist and a strong supporter of Darwin. Stephen Jay Gould wrote that he was, "Astonished and ashamed by the century of mindless recycling that has led to the persistence of these drawings in a large number, if not a majority, of modern textbooks." He made that statement about Haeckel's embryos only recently after having been confronted about it by Michael Behe (the author of *Darwin's Black Box*) in the year 2000. Gould never lifted a finger or a telephone to get those faked drawings out of the science textbooks for twenty years, even though he said he knew they were faked when he did research for his 1977 book *Ontogeny and Phylogeny*. It was considered perfectly acceptable to deceive students all across America, so long as that deception served the purposes of promoting the infallibility and inerrancy of Darwinian Evolutionary Theory. This deception continues in the textbooks to this very day.

Another instance of academic fraud that Wells talks about in his book concerns Bernard Kettlewell's peppered moths. The textbook writers claim Kettlewell's Peppered Moths are legitimate pieces of evidence helping to prove the validity of

Darwinian Evolutionary Theory. Like the faked evidence of Haeckel's embryos, Kettlewell's peppered moth evidence is bogus and therefore it should not be used as positive proof of Darwin's theory in the textbooks. Wells says, "By releasing moths onto nearby tree trunks in daylight, Kettlewell had created an artificial situation that does not exist in nature." In the 1980's, scientists learned that peppered moths do not rest on tree trunks. But the biology textbooks show the peppered moths on tree trunks. The textbook photographers glued and pinned the moths to the tree trunks, so that they could use these false photographs in the textbooks and pawn them off as legitimate unstaged shots of nature in progress. The length to which these textbook photographers and writers will go to promote Darwin's "sacred cow" theory is ridiculous. Our children deserve the truth. But unfortunately, they are not getting the truth in their high school and collegiate biology textbooks.

Two other icons that Wells mentions in his book *Icons of Evolution* are not quite as blatant but are examples of deception and using misleading evidence to perpetuate the myth. The first is the Miller-Urey experiment. In 1953, Miller and Urey were said to have created amino acids, the building blocks of life, in a test tube contraption. According to Wells, they were, "mimicking what were believed to be the natural conditions of the early earth's atmosphere. The telling blow to the Miller-Urey experiment came in the 1970's, when scientists began to conclude that the earth's early atmosphere was nothing like the mixture of gasses used by Miller and Urey.

Instead of being what scientists call a 'reducing' or hydrogen rich environment, the earth's early atmosphere probably consisted of gasses released by volcanoes. Today there is a near consensus among geochemists on this point. But put those volcanic gasses in the Miller-Urey apparatus, and the experiment doesn't work - in other words no building blocks of life. What do textbooks do with this inconvenient fact? By and large, they ignore it and continue to use the Miller-Urey experiment to convince students that scientists have demonstrated an important first step in the origin of life." Once again the textbook writers lie to advance their pro-Darwinian Evolutionary agenda.

Another example of this type of deception that Wells alludes to concerns the beak size of Darwin's finches on the Galappagos Islands. The textbooks noted a 5% increase in average beak size after a severe drought. The U.S. National Academy of Science, which is dogmatic in its pro-macroevolution beliefs, wrote that, "If droughts occur about once every 10 years on the islands, a new species of Finch might arise in only about 200 years." The biology textbooks of course follow suit. They use this as evidence in support of Darwinian Evolution.

"But what the textbooks fail to point out is that the Finches' beaks returned to normal after the rains returned. No net evolution occurred. In fact, several finch species now appear to be merging through hybridization, rather than diverging through natural selection as Darwin's theory requires." Jonathan Wells, who put forth the above quotation, wants the scientific truth to be allowed into the biology textbooks. But currently only the left wing lies and distortions which promote Darwinian theory and its evidences as infallible and inerrant are allowed into the "mainstream" biology textbooks, which are backed by the U.S. National Academy of Sciences.

Evidence supporting Darwinian theory is lacking in many ways. Evolutionists use faulty logic in order to "prove" the theory. Science textbook writers point out the homology of vertebrate limbs. This simply means that humans, frogs, bats, and horses have similar bone structures in their arms or legs. The leftist biology textbook writers use circular reasoning (a logical fallacy) to argue that this similarity in vertebrate limbs proves that these animals (including humans) descended from a common ancestor. They fail to tell the students that this same evidence could just as easily be used to argue that the same intelligent designer created all of these creatures. The homology in vertebrate limbs proves nothing, except that textbook writers enjoy using logical fallacies in order to indoctrinate our children with their left wing lies.

Darwinian Evolutionists will also claim that since there are some similarities between the 24 pairs of ape chromosomes and the 23 pairs of human chromosomes that this means that humans evolved from apes. This evidence could just as easily be interpreted to mean that the same intelligent designer used similar materials in creating humans and apes. It does not prove that one descended from the other.

Where are the "missing links" in Darwinian evolutionary theory? Where are the "transitional forms" which prove that men descended from apes? Let us look at the candidates, which have been put forward as missing links in the macroevolutionary chain.

The first missing link put forward was Java Man. Eugene Dubois discovered Java Man in the early 1890's. It was hailed as the missing link between apes and men and was prominently displayed at the Museum of Natural History in New York as proof positive of Darwin's theory. Eugene Dubois later dismissed his own find as merely an ape known as a "gibbon." The truth finally came out - the whole thing was a mistake in interpretation. The skullcap was that of an ape, which was mistakenly put together with the leg bone of a human. Java Man was no missing link. The New York Museum of Natural History quietly removed Java Man from their displays, but not until 1984.

The next major candidate for the title of missing link was not a case of mistaken interpretation, but was an outright hoax. Charles Dawson discovered "Piltdown Man" in 1912. It was hailed as the missing link until 1953, when a fluorine absorption test proved that one of the two pieces, which composed Piltdown Man, was a relatively modern human skull. The other piece turned out to be an orangutan's jawbone. Like Java Man, Piltdown Man was a case of wishful thinking on the part of hard core Darwinists. They felt the need to pervert the evidence so that it would fit into their particular paradigm.

Finally, the facts won out and Piltdown Man was dismissed as an embarrassing hoax.

The next candidate for the missing link title is known as Lucy the Australopithecine, which was discovered by Donald Johanson in 1974. Leftists in the media and academia immediately jumped to conclusions not supported by the evidence, such as "Lucy must be the long sought after missing link." The truth is that there has been heated debate on this issue within the scientific community. Some anthropologists interpret Lucy's bones to be those of a missing link, while other anthropologists interpret Lucy's bones to be merely those of an extinct ape. For example, British zoologist Solly Zuckermann's scientific study of Australopithecines concluded that they were apes and not ancestors to humans. Also, Charles Oxnard, an anatomy professor at the University of Chicago believes, based on careful scientific study, that Australopithecines are not ancestors to humans, but merely extinct apes. Of course the textbooks suppress Zuckermann's and Oxnard's findings.

There is no universal agreement within the scientific community on how to interpret Lucy's bones. Whether ancient bones such as Lucy's are ancestors of modern humans is a matter of speculative interpretation and opinion. There is no proof that they were human ancestors. For example, the PBS NOVA documentary entitled "Neanderthals on Trial" says that the scientific community is split down the middle over the issue of whether or not Neanderthals were ancestors of modern humans. Some scientists say yes they were and other scientists say no they were not.

As PBS NOVA states, "In the courtroom of scientific opinion, experts look at the same evidence and arrive at very different conclusions." Why can't these differences of scientific opinion be presented in the textbooks and within the public school curriculum?

The most recent candidate for the missing link title is the Dmanisi Skull, discovered in 2001, and prominently displayed on the cover of *National Geographic* magazine in August of 2002. According to an anthropological expert interviewed in 2002 on the PBS Charlie Rose program, there is no way to know for sure whether it is or is not a human ancestor. Even *National Geographic* used the term "could" when talking about the significance of this find. "It *could* be the face of the first human to leave Africa." It "could" be the missing link. It "could" destroy the "out of Africa" paradigm. Many anthropologists believe that the Dmanisi skull is merely the skull of an extinct chimpanzee and is in no way, shape, or form a human ancestor.

The problem is this: The textbooks give our children the false impression that scientists are in total agreement on the topic of human origins, including "missing links" or transitional forms. This is simply not true. The material in the textbooks about human origins is highly speculative theory, which is masqueraded as hard-core infallible fact. Any scientific evidence, which contradicts Darwinian theory, is dismissed as religion or philosophy. This type of political censorship of science in the classroom is appalling. Scientific evidence from both sides of the debate should be allowed into the classroom, the textbooks, and the media.

Suppression of evidence that casts doubt on Darwinian macroevolution is a common way that evolutionists advance their agenda. Darwin believed that all living things evolved gradually from one common ancestor. Therefore, the fossil record, Darwin thought, would eventually show a "tree of life" starting with one trunk (the original ancestor of all life) and gradually branching out to all the diversity of life we have today. Darwin admitted that the fossil record of his day did not support his theory, but he believed that was because not enough fossils had been dug up yet. One hundred and fifty years later Darwin's fossil record problem is even worse. The fossil record shows a "Cambrian Explosion" that explodes Darwin's Theory. According to the Chinese paleontologist Jy Chen, "The Cambrian Explosion turns Darwin's 'tree of life' on its head." The fossil record shows the exact opposite of what Darwin thought it would show.

The "Cambrian Explosion" is the phrase used by paleontologists to describe the fact that all of a sudden in the fossil record there are all the major animal groups fully formed, as if they appeared out of nowhere. There are no fossils predating them in the lower strata, which could be construed as intermediate forms. The late Harvard Paleontologist Stephen Jay Gould admitted that, "The extreme rarity of transitional forms in the fossil record persists as the trade secret of paleontology. The evolutionary trees that adorn our textbooks have data only at the tips and nodes of their branches; the rest is inference, however reasonable, not the evidence of fossils" (Gould, Stephen Jay, 1977. "Natural History" 86, 14.). This Cambrian Explosion contradicts Darwinian Evolutionary Theory, which expected to find fossils evenly distributed and evolving through intermediate forms over millions of years. Animal forms were not supposed to be found created fully formed all at once.

The greatest diversity in animal forms is found at the beginning, and then through time they become less diverse (partially due to extinction and hybridization). Darwin predicted just the opposite in his evolutionary theory: we would begin with only one trunk and gradually over time grow more diverse branches on the tree of life. This Darwinian theory is simply not born out by the facts on and in the ground.

What do the leftist academics in the ivory tower do about these politically incorrect facts? They suppress these facts from the biology textbooks. Most public high school and collegiate biology textbooks do not even mention the Cambrian Explosion. Those few that do mention it fail to adequately explain its significance.

The history and science textbooks also suppress information concerning "the cretaceous flower explosion." They suppress this information in the same way and for the same reasons that they suppress information concerning the "Cambrian Explosion" of animals in the fossil record. These explosions contradict Darwinian Evolutionary Theory, and therefore they are either omitted from the curriculum or barely mentioned without adequately explaining their significance.

National Geographic magazine in July of 2002 called the cretaceous flower explosion "The Big Bloom". *National Geographic's* Michael Klesius wrote, "Just when and how did the first flowering plants emerge? Charles Darwin pondered that question, and paleobotanists are still searching for an answer." They can find no naturalistic explanation for this occurrence. They refuse to even consider the possibility of a supernatural explanation, such as: God created the flowers and that is why they appear all at once without any precursors in the fossil record. Since Charles Darwin was not willing to accept any supernatural explanations, even when the evidence led in that direction, he called this issue the "abominable mystery" of flowering plants.

Even Darwin himself admitted that he had no credible explanation for the "abominable mystery" of flowering plants. No natural explanation is credible because the flowering plants appear all at once without ancestors in the fossil record predating them. With no naturalistic explanation the only thing left to choose from is a supernatural explanation, i.e. God created the flowers. This distinct possibility, and only logical explanation based upon the evidence in the fossil record, should not be banned from the curriculum because of the anti-Biblical bigotry of the National Academy of Sciences.

Could it be that God created the animals in what paleontologists call the "Cambrian Explosion"? Could it be that God created the flowers in what the paleobotanists call the "cretaceous flower explosion"? Could it be that

God was wise and correct and that naturalistic human scientists were foolish and in error?

Because of the dogmatically pro-Darwin National Academy of Science, these questions are not permitted to be asked. The Darwinists ban these questions from the textbooks. Liberals believe that these questions should not be protected by the First Amendment, but that computer-generated child-porn on the Internet should be protected by the First Amendment. Many liberal judges on the 9th Circuit Court of Appeals in California believe that Darwinian macro-evolutionary theory should be taught as fact in the public schools, but that the Pledge of Allegiance should be banned in the public schools. These Darwinian leftists can't stand the phrase, "One Nation Under God." They probably wouldn't have a problem with the pledge if it said, "One Nation Under Darwin, Marx, and Freud."

Our Founding Fathers wrote in the Declaration of Independence that we are endowed by our "Creator." Our Founding Fathers wrote in the U.S. Constitution the words, "In the year of our Lord one thousand seven hundred and eighty-seven." The Framers of the U.S. Constitution, if they were alive today, would fight full force against the Darwinian leftists who refuse to acknowledge, or even let students in the classroom acknowledge the Creator God.

Micro vs. Macro Evolution

In order to fully understand the debate over evolution, one must be able to define some key terms and make some very important distinctions between different words. First there is no debate over microevolution. Conservative Christians as well as left wing atheists agree that microevolution takes place. Microevolution refers to changes that take place within a species by way of natural selection or selective breeding. An example would be the breeding of dogs to get different types of dogs. In the end, they are all still dogs that can interbreed with other types of dogs. They are, at the end of the day, the same species, even though there is great variability in their traits among the different types. Another example of microevolution is bacteria becoming resistant to an antibiotic because of a mutation. The bacteria are still bacteria.

There are three key points to remember concerning microevolution. Number one, it always results from a loss of genetic information. It never results from an addition of genetic information. Number two, no new species is created; bacteria remain bacteria, and a dog remains a dog (The change takes place within the species.). Number three; conservative Christians and liberal atheists both agree that microevolution takes place.

Where does the disagreement come about? The debate is not about microevolution, on which everyone agrees. The debate is over the theory of macroevolution. Macroevolution, first proposed by Darwin, states that all the diversity of life on earth today derives from one, or a few, common ancestors. Macroevolution promotes the idea that molecules turned into animals and animals turned into man. Man evolved from apes, and apes evolved from the primordial ooze. Macroevolution encompasses changes from one species to another species that can no longer interbreed with the species from which it is descended. According to the current orthodoxy, macroevolution takes place through the random chance of genetic mutations.

The medical doctor turned novelist, Michael Crichton, wrote about what he termed the "problems of evolution." He proclaimed, "There's the coordination problem. If you believe the current theory, then all the wonderful complexity of life is nothing but the accumulation of chance events - a bunch of genetic accidents strung together. Yet when we look closely at animals, it appears as if many elements must have evolved simultaneously. Take bats, which have echolocation-they navigate by sound. To do that, many things must evolve. Bats need a specialized apparatus to make sounds, they need specialized ears to hear echoes, they need specialized brains to interpret the sounds, and they need specialized bodies to dive and swoop and catch insects. If all these things don't evolve simultaneously, there's no advantage. And to imagine all these things happen purely by chance is like imagining that a tornado can hit a junkyard and assemble the parts into a working 747 airplane. It's very hard to believe."

Intelligent Design

A scientist by the name of Michael Behe has answered some of these perplexing questions by proposing a theory called "intelligent design." This theory concludes that the fossil record as well as the "irreducible complexity" of the inner workings of the cell lead us to only one logical conclusion: that biological diversity is the result of the work of an intelligent designer.

If one walks down the beach and sees written in the sand "Susan loves Johnny" one concludes not that it came about by natural causes such as the waves, but that it came about by an intelligent designer. A literate human being wrote it in the sand.

If one finds a wristwatch on the beach, one does not conclude that it was made by natural causes such as the waves crashing on the shore. One concludes that it is so complex that only an intelligent designer could have made it.

What are the mathematical chances that you could take hundreds of bowls of alphabet soup throw them into a "primordial soup" and expect them by random chance to spell out the complete text of Shakespeare's *Hamlet*? And how much more complicated are the messages in human DNA compared to Shakespeare's *Hamlet*? The chemicals within DNA are like letters of the alphabet, both must be arranged in a precisely correct sequence in order to create a meaningful information packed message. There is no naturalistic process that can create information, and DNA contains more information than the complete text of Shakespeare's *Hamlet.* Objective mathematicians, like William Dembski of Baylor University, and experts in probability, know that Darwin's macro-evolutionary theory is ridiculous.

In addition there are 20 types of amino acids, which are akin to the 26 letters in the English alphabet. They must be arranged in the precisely correct sequence in order to form the proteins necessary for life. They do not and cannot arrange themselves randomly by chance. They take strict marching orders from the encoded messages in the DNA. Likewise, if letters in the English alphabet align themselves randomly one will end up with gibberish, not meaningful messages.

Physicists Stephen Wolfram, author of *A New Kind of Science*, Ed Fredkin, a former director of the Computer Science laboratory at the Massachusetts Institute of Technology, and Tom Siegfried, author of *The Bit and the Pendulum*, all believe that the universe runs on the equivalent of a computer program and not by random chance. Siegfried calls it the "New physics of information". At the present time, most leftists within the scientific community suppress this new paradigm because to give it publicity would overturn their naturalistic Darwinian/Bohrian paradigm, which is based upon the foundations of random chance.

Another reason why the left wingers who control the academic scientific orthodoxy of the present day suppress this "new kind of science", that the universe is run by the equivalent of a computer program, is because it begs a profound question. That question is, who designed the computer program? Who wrote the code?

Does Bill Gates use random chance to design his software or does he use highly intelligent designers called computer programmers? The left wing is afraid that the people will answer the question, who wrote the code on which the universe runs by saying, "God the Creator." This answer, according to the left wing science juggernaut, is simply not allowed. Therefore, in their opinion, this line of reasoning must be suppressed. That is why this information may never make it into the public high school and collegiate textbooks.

Intelligent Design Theory is being selectively banned from mainstream science. Scientists allow it to be used in hopes of finding intelligent life forms in outer space (The Search for Extraterrestrial Intelligence Program or S.E.T.I.) but they do not allow it into the biology textbooks where it would contradict the Darwinian macro evolutionary orthodoxy. In the S.E.T.I. Program they listen for messages from outer space. They determine if it was an intelligently designed message or just random clutter, by looking for definite patterns that go above and beyond the background noise in their complexity. Of course, they have not found an intelligently designed message yet, but they are hoping. They find it easier to have faith in aliens from outer space than in the God of the Bible. But the fact that they use intelligent design inferences in one field of science but not the other shows their left wing liberal bias. They are not against the design inference per se; they are only against it when it lends credence to the existence of a creator God.

Whenever proponents of intelligent design theory ask for equal time in the curriculum along side Darwinian macro-evolutionary theory, they are told by the Darwinists that, "Intelligent Design is not science. It is religion, and therefore, it should not be allowed into the science curriculum." This atheistic left wing argument is patently absurd. Science is supposed to be about finding the truth through observation, experiment and logical reasoning. As you have read earlier, evolution is a theory that cannot be tested under the conditions that existed when the universe was formed; no evidence exists of one species changing into another or new genetic material forming from existing genetic information. If science is supposed to be about a search for the truth then why can't evidence from both viewpoints be presented, analyzed, and debated by scholarly students who can then decide which theory to believe. The type of censorship and suppression that dogmatic Darwinian Evolutionists promote goes against the very definition of science.

Though Darwinian evolutionists will say that presenting intelligent design theory is religion, the truth is that they promote their own religion, known as naturalistic "Secular Humanism" (see the "Secular Humanist Manifesto"-many of its signatories are prominent left wing scientists). When being presented with the myth that Darwinian Evolution is fact, students cannot help but question any theological ideals that they may have been taught at home. With this "evidence" a student might conclude there is no God, no purpose to each person's existence, no absolute right and wrong, and can justify any actions with a Darwinian self-perservation motive. This is exactly what happened when Joseph Stalin was presented with the writings of Darwin.

Darwinists and Liberals say that God has nothing to do with science, and therefore God should be completely censored from the science curriculum. If it is true that God has nothing to do with science then why does the world's leading astro-physicist Stephen Hawking end his science book on physics, *A Brief History of Time*, by invoking the name of God. Hawking writes, "If we do discover a complete [unified field] theory...then we would know the mind of God." Hawking and Einstein understood that God created the laws of science. That is why Einstein said in a scientific debate, "God does not play dice." According to the naturalistic, secular, leftists who control much of science in the academy today, those portions of Hawking's and Einstein's work must be suppressed from the textbooks and the student body. The naturalistic secular paradigm cannot abide a meaningful creator God. These leftists philosophically prefer the nihilism of meaningless random chance.

The left wingers who control the science and history textbooks are not promoting objective scientific truth. They are promoting left wing lies and distortions in order to support their worldview. Darwin's macro-evolutionary theory (molecules to man evolution-we came from an apelike ancestor) forms the foundation of the modern left wing world-view. If it tumbles all else in the left wing world-view will fall. It is a shame that a truthful Chinese Paleontologist can accurately summarize the scientific status quo in American academia today by stating, "In China we can criticize Darwin but not the government. In America you can criticize the government but not Darwin."

9
Kennewick Man

"Paradigm was just another word for a model, but as scientists used it the term meant something more, a world view. A larger way of seeing the world. Paradigm shifts were said to occur whenever science made a major change in its view of the world."

-Michael Crichton, Jurassic Park

On July 28, 1996, two college students, Will Thomas and David Deacy, found an almost complete human skeleton, including the skull, along the banks of the Columbia River near Kennewick, Washington (Washington State). They reported their find to the police. The police reported the find to Floyd Johnson, the coroner of Benton County, Washington. Floyd Johnson called in the forensic anthropologist James Chatters.

Chatters inspected the skull and determined that it was a male Caucasian. At first Chatters thought that since Kennewick Man is Caucasian he couldn't be very old. But something about these bones caught Chatter's eye that really intrigued him. In his hipbone was imbedded a stone-age spear point. Chatters immediately sent a piece of Kennewick Man's bone to the lab to be radiocarbon dated. When the date came back as 9,300 years old, that is when all the trouble began. Chatters knew he had come across one of the archeological finds of the century, but he also knew that certain groups might want to suppress the find for political reasons. The controversy was about to begin.

Why was this find so significant? First, there are fewer than five intact skeletons older than 9,000 years ever found in North America. But even more significant than that was the shape of the skull and the crural index of the femur bones. The skull was not shaped like American Indian skulls. The skull lacked the mongoloid racial characteristics that all American Indian and oriental people have. Instead, the skull was shaped like those of Europeans or those with Caucasoid racial characteristics. The femur bones showed a crural index consistent with Caucasoid peoples, not mongoloid peoples. This was clearly not an American Indian. The problem was that white people were not supposed to be in the New World 9,000 years ago.

According to the traditional scientific and historical paradigm, white people did not enter the New World until 1492 A.D. when Christopher Columbus "discovered" America. Of course, this paradigm had to be revised a few years ago when archeologists found Viking settlements on Newfoundland, Canada, which predated 1492 A.D. But Leif Ericson's Viking settlements only dated back to 1000A.D. So these discoveries pushed back the paradigm only about 400-500 years. So the textbooks say white people have been in the New World for only the last 1,000 years or so.

The traditional scientific and historical paradigm tells us that mongoloid Indian people are the "Native Americans," and that they came into the New World over the Bering Strait Land Bridge. The orthodoxy is that these Indians from

Asia were the first human beings to enter the Americas. This is called the "Clovis First" theory. (The term "Clovis" came from Clovis, New Mexico where some ancient spear points were found.)

This paradigm of the peopling of the New World has been shattered by new archeological finds. But these new archeological finds (including Kennewick Man) have been suppressed from the high school and collegiate U.S. and World History textbooks. Why are the textbooks and the news media suppressing Kennewick Man and the other archeological finds that destroy the "Clovis First" theory? Because-regardless of the facts-it would be "politically incorrect" to strip Indians of their "Native American" status. Being first gives them the political credibility to demand special legal rights (including lucrative gambling casino rights) and to demand that sports teams, professional, college and high school change their names (no Indian names allowed!). Without the mantle of being the first, they would lose much of their political clout to further their political agenda. Not all Indians believe in the political correctness movement and in the suppression of scientific finds such as Kennewick Man; in fact, most do not. However, many powerful activist Indians do indeed believe in those things.

Mr. Chatters wanted to send Kennewick Man to the Smithsonian Institution for further study by the top scientists in the world, but he would not get the chance for further study of the bones. No one would.

The Umatilla Indian Tribe demanded that Kennewick Man be given to them immediately for reburial in an undisclosed location. They wanted all scientific study of the bones to cease and desist. They said they had the legal right to the bones under NAGPRA (The Native American Graves Protection and Repatriation Act of 1990), because Kennewick Man predated 1492 and that fact proved that Kennewick Man must be their ancestor. Remember white people weren't supposed to be in North America prior to Columbus in 1492.

In 1996, while this controversy unfolded, the President of the United States was Bill Clinton. Bill Clinton's appointee and good friend Bruce Babbitt, was Secretary of the Interior. The Colonel in charge of the Army Corps of Engineers had to obey orders given to him by Commander in Chief Bill Clinton. Bill Clinton was found guilty of lying under oath about sex. This time Bill Clinton would orchestrate a deceptive cover-up of Kennewick Man, something of even greater historical importance than the incident for which he was impeached. Kennewick Man's skull has more historical significance than Monica Lewinsky's mouth. But the media preferred to discuss Lewinsky Woman as opposed to Kennewick Man.

The U.S. Army Corps of Engineers controlled the land where Kennewick Man was found. Chatters was forced to give up the bones to the government's Army Corps of Engineers. The Clinton administration decided to give the bones back to the Indians for reburial.

The bones would be lost to science forever. In order to save Kennewick Man for scientific study, eight scientists, including Douglas Owsley of the Smithsonian Institution, sued the federal government in an attempt to stop the Clinton administration from suppressing the evidence (*Bonnichsen et. al. v. U.S.*, civil no. 96-1481 JE, District of Oregon).

The Indians told one of the highest-ranking men in the Army Corps of Engineers that they wanted all publicity concerning Kennewick Man to cease and desist. This high-ranking official in the Army Corps of Engineers told the Indians words to the effect that he would see to it that the publicity would end. James Chatters was furious that the Army Corps of Engineers was promising to "stifle the news media." Chatters said, "Haven't you heard of the first amendment to the Constitution?" One of the Corps staffers said, "The first amendment doesn't apply in NAGPRA cases." Chatters responded, "The first amendment always applies." Chatters is the Indiana Jones of the Kennewick Man find. He has been trying valiantly from the beginning to allow the American people to have access to the truth.

Kennewick Man was not the first skeleton to be suppressed. Chatters said, "In 1991, the 12,800 year old Buhl Skeleton had been turned over to the Shoshone-Bannocks of Fort Hall after only one incomplete study by a graduate student; In 1993, a 9,000 year old partial male skeleton found in Hourglass Cave, Colorado, had been similarly treated." That is why "Owsley went all out for Kennewick Man." Owsley and Chatters wanted knowledge of the evidence to win out over suppression of the evidence.

The only argument the Indians had to link Kennewick Man with them was their "oral history." According to NAGPRA if a skull was found, one must first determine if it was affiliated with a local Indian tribe. If it was, it should be turned over to the control of that tribe. If it was determined not to be affiliated with any American Indian tribe, the scientists could keep it for study.

All the scientific evidence, skull morphology, and the crural index of the femur bones and dental evidence, indicate that Kennewick Man is not affiliated with any modern American Indian tribe. But the Clinton administration intentionally ignored this evidence and made its decision to give the Indians the bones, based upon the Indians' oral history. The Indians said that their oral history tells them that they were always in North America. They did not migrate from Asia or anywhere else. Their ancestors were created in North America at the beginning of time. This oral history was the pretext used by Bruce Babbitt, Secretary of the Interior and friend of Clinton's, to decide that the Indians, not the scientists, were entitled to control the bones. The Indians had the right to rebury the bones in an undisclosed location, or destroy them for that matter. Babbitt and Clinton decided that the scientists should have no right to study these bones. The pretext was the oral history argument.

As I pointed out earlier in this book, oral history is often based in fact. Homer's *Iliad* was first passed down orally. Schliemann found Troy because he took seriously the Homeric oral history. But the key is that the oral history must be based on a longstanding tradition passed down from generation to generation by honest individuals. There must be no 180-degree turns in the story by dishonest individuals motivated by political self-interest.

Amy Dansie of the Nevada State Museum told James Chatters, "We have the Paiutes down here, which by their own oral traditions came recently into Nevada. They talk about taking the land from the Zaideka-Tule Eaters-who they call the 'redheaded giants.' But the [ancient Caucasoid shaped] skeletons are at risk, because Federal agencies are giving in to the new claims by the Paiutes that they were created in their present territories and have 'always been here.' " Red-headed giants could only have been Caucasoid. Only Europeans have red hair. The skulls in that area, which predate the Indian mongoloid migration, are Caucasoid in shape. The scientific evidence does support the original truthful Indian oral history; it does not support the recently fabricated "oral history."

The Clinton administration had the Army Corps of Engineers strip the bones from Chatters. Because of Owsley's lawsuit, the Clinton administration could not immediately give the bones to the Indians. That would have to wait for the legal dispute to play itself out. The court ordered the federal government to carefully protect and secure the bones until the court reached a final decision.

Instead of protecting the bones, the Feds under Clinton allowed people, including hardcore activist Indians, to visit and physically handle the bones. Shortly thereafter, it was learned that two femur bones were missing. Some people may conclude that the bones were stolen. The Feds tried to deny that any bones were missing, but

Chatters could prove it. Before the Feds stripped the bones from him, Chatters videotaped all of them. Chatters' videotape was indisputable proof that the two femur bones had existed when he turned over the bones, but that they no longer existed. Remember, forensic pathologists often use the femur bones to determine the race of a homicide victim whose flesh has already rotted away. But this was not even the worst incident of the Clintonian cover up of Kennewick man.

According to the *Washington Post* and the *Philadelphia Inquirer*, Clinton ordered the Army Corps of Engineers to destroy and literally cover up the Kennewick Man discovery site along the Columbia River in Washington State. Chatters and others kept finding more ancient bones there every time they went back to dig around the area. If Kennewick Man had a wife, children, or a comrade who was buried in that same area, it would make the situation worse for the politically correct paradigm, if those bones were uncovered.

The U.S. House of Representatives and the U.S. Senate voted against letting the Army Corps of Engineers destroy and cover up the Kennewick Man discovery site with rubble. The Corps decided not to cover up the site. Then, with orders from Clinton reversing that decision, on April 6, 1998, the Army Corps of Engineers, in a sneak attack, brought in helicopters and heavy equipment to drop 500 tons of rocks, rubble, and dirt on the Kennewick Man discovery site. "Corps documents, including a November 28, 1997 letter to the National Marine Fisheries Service, say that, 'Concern on the part of the White House' led to the Corps' dubious plan" to bury the Kennewick

Man discovery site under 500 tons of rock, dirt and rubble (*National Review*-3-8-99, "Remains of the Day-Politics Buries a Key Archeological Find" by John J. Miller).

As a result of this action, the 8 scientists added destruction of evidence to their lawsuit against the federal government. On August 30, 2002, "The court ruled that the Army Corps of Engineers violated the National Historic Preservation Act when it buried the skeleton's discovery site."

Kennewick Man is not the only ancient Caucasoid skull found in the New World. A skull called "Spirit Cave Man" was found in Nevada. Spirit Cave Man dates to 9,400 years old. James C. Chatters says on page 196 of his book *Ancient Encounters-Kennewick Man and the First Americans* that Spirit Cave Man "was most similar to the medieval Norse and the Ainu." The Norse are northern European Caucasoids. The Ainu are what anthropologists call "Japanese Caucasoids." Only 100 full-blooded Ainu exist today. They are Caucasians that settled the islands of Japan prior to the oriental mongoloids that today compose 99% of the population of Japan. The Indians demand that Spirit Cave Man be turned over to them for reburial in an undisclosed location. As of the writing of this book, he has not yet been turned over. The scientists say he is not affiliated with any modern American Indian tribe and therefore he should not be turned over to them.

Doug Owsley, of the Smithsonian Institution, says that, "The fossil record shows us that people very much like modern Indians appeared in North America by around six thousand B.C" (8,000 years ago Mongoloid Indians arrived in North America). Walter Neves seconded this opinion by saying that, "Before seven thousand B.C. [9,000 years ago], there are no mongoloid Indian skulls in the Americas." But there are Europeanoid and Africanoid skulls, which predate the mongoloid Indian skulls in the Americas.

In Southern Brazil, in the Logoa Santa Region, archeologists discovered Luzia (Lapa Vermelha IV), a human skeleton including the skull that dated back to 10,600 B.C. Walter Neves and all the scientists who inspected the bones, American and Brazilian, agreed that the skull was that of an African, and definitely not that of a mongoloid Indian.

Also, DNA testing on Spirit Cave man shows halo group x. This proves that Spirit Cave Man had European Caucasoid ancestry, because halo group x only exists in Caucasoid populations. So the evidence from North America and South America show that mongoloid Indians were not the first people in the New World. Caucasoids probably from Europe and Africans probably from Australia or Africa were in the Americas prior to the people we know as Indians. The title "Native Americans" conferred on the mongoloid Indians may be politically correct, but it does not seem to be factually correct.

Professor Tom Dillehay from the University of Kentucky engaged in a spectacular archeological dig in Mt. Verde, Chile. In this dig he found a human habitation site that predated the Clovis finds in North America. Dillehay destroyed the Clovis first paradigm. At first, the top archeologists in the United States did not want to give up their politically correct Clovis paradigm that said: Mongoloid Indians were first and they came in from Asia through Alaska. They then spread out and down through all the Americas to the tip of South America. The next major migration was that of Europeans after 1492. End of story. Tom Dillehay shattered this paradigm into pieces. For years the "Clovis Police" viciously attacked Dillehay. The left wing academics did not want to have to change their paradigm. "Dillehay must be a charlatan or an incompetent." "There must be contamination in his dating." They attacked him and gave him the cold shoulder at academic symposiums and conferences.

Finally, the tide changed in 1997, when a blue ribbon panel of America's top academic archeologists visited Dillehay's site in Mt. Verde, Chile. They went in skeptical. They came out convinced. Mt. Verde, Chile was a legitimate human habitation site, which predated the oldest North American Clovis site by 1,000 years. The Clovis first paradigm had officially been destroyed. However, the current U.S. and World History textbooks refuse to change their politically correct but factually incorrect treatment of this subject of the peopling of the Americas. Even the History Channel's video, "In Search of History-The First Americans," completely censored out Kennewick Man and Spirit Cave Man. They don't want people to know about them. The PBS Nova Video "Mystery of the First Americans" did not censor out Kennewick Man, but it did censor out the fact that two femur bones were "missing" and that the

Clinton administration destroyed and covered up the Kennewick Man discovery site with 500 tons of rock and dirt. They don't want the masses to know about these facts. They feel the need to suppress.

Graham Hancock points out in his book *Fingerprints of the Gods* that there are Olmec Statues carved out of giant rocks that contain the faces of bearded Caucasoids and others with faces that are clearly black African in their physical features. This is ancient artistic evidence that blacks and whites were in the New World back before the height of the Aztecs and Inca Empires. Hancock says that "political correctness" forces scholars in academia to ignore this evidence. Only mongoloid Indians are supposed to be in the Americas at that time.

Hancock also points out that the god of the Aztecs, Quetzlcoatl, was always portrayed and explained as a pale faced bearded Caucasoid. The Indians of that region cannot grow full beards. That is why when Cortes came to conquer the Aztecs, the Aztecs thought the pale-faced bearded Cortes was their god Quetzlcoatl. That is one of the reasons a small band of Spaniards under Cortes was able to conquer the huge Aztec empire.

The Spanish Explorer Garcia De La Vega, who served under Pizzaro, asked the Incas if they had built the spectacular city of Tiahuanaco, Bolivia. They said, "No." "It was built thousands of years before our time." Bolivian scholar Arthur Posnansky spent 50 years of his life studying Tiahuanaco. He came to the conclusion, based upon astronomical alignments and precession of the equinoxes, that Tiahuanaco was 17,000 years old. For years orthodox scholars refused to believe Posnansky, because to do so would require a shattering of their preciously held paradigm concerning the peopling of the New World.

How did European and African peoples get to the New World at such an early date? Thor Heyerdahl answered this question. Heyerdahl did not appreciate left wing anti-hero academics that thought our ancient ancestors were knuckle-dragging ape-men living in caves. He realized that humans settled Australia in ancient times and that there was no land bridge to be crossed on foot. He knew that humans used boats, ocean going vessels to cross the open seas. The academics scoffed at Heyerdahl's thesis. They thought that people at that time had not evolved enough intellectually to be able to build ocean-going vessels. So Heyerdahl proved the ivory tower academics to be wrong.

In 1970, Heyerdahl built and used a small reed boat to personally cross the oceans from continent to continent. Heyerdahl proved that ancient man had the technology to cross the oceans. (Heyerdahl is also famous for a book he wrote entitled *The Kon Tiki Expedition*, which chronicled some of his pre-"Ra Expedition" adventures.)

A German scientist Dr. Svetla Balabanova inspected a 3,000-year-old Egyptian mummy called Henut Taui. She discovered that the body contained large traces of cocaine and nicotine. She found the same thing in other ancient Egyptian mummies. This led her to conclude something very startling, which has been suppressed from the mainstream of academia:

ancient Egyptians must have had some level of cross-oceanic trade with the New World of the Americas, because coca and tobacco (nicotine) only grow in the New World. They were completely unknown to most Europeans and Asians until Sir Walter Raleigh brought them back from America to Europe many centuries later.

Dennis Stanford of the Smithsonian Institution (one of the eight scientists suing the government in the Kennewick Man case) says that Europeans migrated to the New World prior to the Indians from Asia. Stanford says that these Europeans came over on boats. Bruce Bradley, a scientist from Colorado and a stone tool expert, agrees with Dennis Stanford. The two plan to write a book promoting and defending their thesis, which may prove in the long run to be the replacement to fill the vacuum left by the destruction of the "Clovis-first" paradigm.

U.S. history textbooks do not mention Kennewick Man or Spirit Cave Man. U.S. history textbooks do not mention Dennis Stanford's thesis of Europeans first via boats along the North Atlantic ice sheets and into the Eastern seaboard of the United States. The textbooks reinforce the politically correct view that mongoloid Indians were first and that they came across the Bering Land Bridge. They don't let the facts get in their way. It is time for the suppression of information to stop. It is time for the truth to be revealed.

Postscript to this story: *U.S. News and World Report* (December 16, 2002) reported that a Caucasoid shaped human skeleton discovered in 1959 near Mexico City recently carbon dated to 13,000 years of age. This find lends even more credence to the idea that Europeans settled the New World prior to the Indians from Asia.

10
Conclusion

"If you don't know history, you don't know anything."

-Michael Crichton - Timeline

The politically correct liberals who control the nightly news broadcasts have suppressed important aspects of world history concerning militant Islam. That is why to many Americans the tragic events of September 11, 2001, came as a shock, as a surprise, as an aberration from the norm. Those who lacked knowledge of military, political, and religious history of this world had to view the events of September 11 in a vacuum without context and without precedent. Those who had read Creasy's *The Fifteen Decisive Battles Of The World* viewed September 11th not as an aberration from the norm but the norm itself. Those students of military and religious history could view September 11th within a larger historical context, the context of a continuous struggle between East and West, between militant Islam and Christendom. (Many Muslims believe in peaceful co-existence with non-Muslims. In this chapter, I am referring only to those Muslims who are militant and financial supporters of Osama Bin Laden's anti-Western terrorist ideology and policies. This chapter does not refer to those who believe in and practice Islam as a religion of peace, but merely those who believe in and practice Islam as a religion of submission. This chapter refers only to those Muslims who believe in a Taliban style of Islam that all must submit to or be put to the sword.)

In 732 A.D., Muslim armies tried to take over Western Europe. They were defeated by the Christian armies led by Charles "The Hammer" Martel at the Battle of Tours in France. After this defeat the Muslim armies retreated back to Spain and eventually to northern Africa. Charles Martel's grandson was Charlemagne, who Christianized the last remaining European barbarians and brought Europe out of the Dark Ages. As Creasy tells us, if it weren't for Martel's victory at Tours, we in the United States and Western Europe would either be dead or Muslim. We would be reading the Koran not the Bible. Our women's faces would be covered. We would be speaking Arabic languages not English. We would not have the freedoms and standard of living we currently enjoy.

The historian Arnold wrote that the Christian victory over the Muslims at Tours ranks, "among those signal deliverances which have affected for centuries the happiness of mankind." Gibbon reaffirmed the importance of Charles the Hammer Martel's victory at the Battle of Tours by stating that it, "rescued our ancestors of Britain and our neighbors of Gaul from the civil and religious yoke of the Koran." Hans Delbruck, in his commentary on the Battle of Tours wrote that there was "no more important battle in world history."

Before the "multiculturalism" and "political correctness" movements took over academia, many historians in the West surmised that Divine intervention was to be credited for the Christian victory over the Muslims at Tours. Some called it miraculous. Eggenberger wrote, "It was one of the rare times in the Middle Ages when infantry held its ground against mounted attack." The Christian foot soldiers held firm in their formations, against the mounted Arab onslaught. Victor Davis Hanson points out that, "Charles became known as 'the Hammer'- an allusion to the Biblical hammerer, Judas Maccabaeus, whose Israelite armies through Divine intervention had smashed the Syrians."

Between 1096 and 1291 A.D., the Crusades took place. In the First Crusade, the Christians took over the Holy Land including Jerusalem. But in the Second Crusade, Saladin unified the Muslims in a Holy War against the Christians, and he took back Jerusalem. In the Third Crusade, Saladin was able to fight Richard the Lionhearted to a standstill. Saladin became a Muslim icon. Today painted on buildings in Palestine are the names and likenesses of three highly revered Muslims: Mohammed, Saladin, and Osama Bin Laden (James Reston, Jr. *Warriors of God: Richard the Lionhearted and Saladin in the Third Crusade.* C-Span II Book TV-Aug. 25, 2001, and illustrated by a photograph in *Newsweek*-December 30, 2002, page 46.).

In 1529 and 1683 A.D. the Muslim armies tried again to take over Western Europe. Both of these Muslim armies were stopped and defeated at the gates of Vienna, Austria. Christendom was once again saved.

The Muslim armies tried to take over and destroy Israel in 1967, in what is known as the Six Day War. The U.S.-backed Israeli military won the war rapidly, and in so doing saved the existence of the state of Israel.

Muslim armies today realize that the United States and Israel cannot be defeated in a traditional war, because of the West's vast superiority in the areas of air power and technology. Therefore the Muslim armies, such as Al-Qaeda and others, have reverted to guerilla-style terrorist attacks against Americans and Israelis. They know that this style of Jihad (Holy War) is at times politically effective. In the 1980s, the United States pulled all Marines out of Beirut, Lebanon, after one terrorist suicide truck bomber killed hundreds of U.S. Marines. The U.S. pulled out of Somalia after a U.S. Army Ranger Black Hawk helicopter was shot down and a U.S. soldier was dragged through the streets of Mogadishu. Bin Laden and his ilk believe that a few September 11ths will force America to pull out its financial and military support from Israel.

Even if America stopped supporting Israel, Bin Laden, Al Qaeda, and their ilk would still enjoy killing Americans for two additional reasons. First, they believe all "infidels" (non-Muslims) should be killed in a "jihad" (holy war). Second, they hate Americans because they are jealous of the success of Western Civilization.

It is knowledge of history that allows one to comprehend the events of September 11, 2001. When September 11th is viewed in a vacuum, it is incomprehensible.

Victor Davis Hanson, in his book *Carnage and Culture*, points out that the West can only be defeated by other Westerners. The West can only defeat itself, if it chooses to take a masochistic or suicidal path. The East and all non-Western cultures are too weak to ever completely defeat the West in a major military conflict. Only the West can defeat itself by giving up the ghost religiously, politically, and culturally.

For our Civilization to survive, we must revive belief in the positive heroes of Western culture, which include Columbus, Custer, and Crockett. For a person with a negative hero frequently becomes self-destructive. And a person with no hero at all frequently becomes apathetic, and goes adrift like a rudderless ship, lost in a sea of humanity. We must politically defend our military from liberal social engineering that threatens to weaken our combat effectiveness. We must revive belief in the God of the Bible and not the god called "mother earth." We must revive belief in Einstein's truism that "God does not play dice." We must revive belief in the humanity of our ancient ancestors, as well as our unborn children, and not let the liberals convince us that our ancestors were apes and that our unborn children should be aborted. We must intellectually challenge the liberals who currently control much of the "scientific" community. We must reveal the truth about who the first people were that settled the New World. The facts must be allowed to speak for themselves.

The liberals suppress and sever our true history in order to destroy our Judeo-Christian culture. An example is the fact that many textbook writers have substituted BCE (before the common era) and CE (common era) for B.C. (Before Christ) and A.D. (Anno Domini-the year of our Lord). They are removing Christ from the calendar and from his pivotal place in history. Solzhenitsyn was right when he said, "In order to destroy a people, you must first sever their roots." Michael Crichton was correct when he wrote, "History is the power to define a whole society." The bottom line is that we and our culture will be destroyed if we do not take back and successfully defend our history.

What must we do to take back our history? We must counter the liberal lies. We must counter the lies of commission as well as the lies of omission. We must replace the lies with the truth. And that truth will surely set us free.

Bibliography

Chapter 1

Boorstin, Daniel and Kelley, Brooks. *A History of the United States.* Massachusetts: Prentice Hall, 2002.

Dinsmore, Herman H. *All The News That Fits.* New York: Arlington House, 1970.

Dowd, Maureen. "Folderol, Humbug, Balderdash." *Cincinnati Enquirer* January 2, 1995.

Goldberg, Bernard. *Bias -- A CBS Insider Exposes How The Media Distorts The News.* Washington D.C.: Regnery Publishing, Inc., 2002. p. 126, 208-214

John 8:32, King James Version, *The Holy Bible.*

Karlgard, Rich. "Incomparable Carver." *Forbes.* March 18, 2002. p. 39

Kuhn, Thomas. *The Structure of Scientific Revolutions.* Chicago: University of Chicago, 1962, Revised 1970.

Leo, John. "The PC Attack On Heroism." *U.S. News & World Report.* October 31, 1994. p. 36

Leo, John. "The Hijacking of American History." *U.S. News.* Nov. 14, 1994. p. 36

Leo, John. "All The News That Fits Our Biases." *U.S. News* June 10, 1996. p. 26

Leo, John. "The First Crack In The Wall." *U.S. News*, March 10, 1997. p. 19

Leo, John. "A Blogs Bark Has Bite." *U.S. News*. May 13, 2002. p. 48

Leo, John. "Running Away With The Law." *U.S. News*. May 20, 2002. p. 47

Plato. *The Republic.* New York: J.M. Dent and Sons Ltd., 1948. p. 84, 207-208

Schoch, Robert. *Voices of the Rocks-A Scientist Looks At Catastrophes and Ancient Civilizations.* New York: Harmony Books, 1999. p. 12-14

Veith, Gene Edward, "Group Thinkers-The Smithsonian Rejects A Grant That Celebrates Great Individuals." *World.* Feb. 23, 2002. p. 16

Chapter 2

Eggenberger, David. *An Encyclopedia of Battles.* New York: Dover Publications, 1985.

Eliot, T.S. *The Hollow Men.* New York: Harcourt Brace Jovanovich, 1980. p. 810-812. Adventures in English Literature Heritage Edition

Kidd, J.H. *Personal Recollections of a Cavalryman with Custer's Michigan Brigade in the Civil War.* New York: Bantam Books, 1991.

Kinsley, D.A. *Custer Favor the Bold.* New York: Promontory Press, 1988.

Lewis, C.S. *The Abolition of Man.* New York: Simon and Schuster Inc., 1996.

Longacre, Edward. *Custer and His Wolverines.* Conshohocken, PA: Combined Publishing, 1997.

Riggs, David. *East of Gettysburg-Custer vs. Stuart.* Gettysburg: The Old Army Press, 1970.

Storrick, W.C. *The Battle of Gettysburg.* Harrisburg: Mount Pleasant Press, 1955.

Turner, Ted. *Gettysburg*-The Film. Atlanta: Turner Home Entertainment, 1993.

Urwin, Gregory. *Custer Victorious.* Lincoln Nebraska: University of Nebraska Press, 1983.

Chapter 3

Asher, Lisa. “The Expanded, Updated, and Star-Studded Story of a Mexican Civil War known as the Alamo.” *The Baylor Line.* Fall 2003. p. 55-59

Biffle, Kent. "De la Pena Renounced." *The Dallas Morning News.* November 15, 1998.

Biffle, Kent. "Memoir about Davy Crockett Raises Some Expert's Eyebrows." *Dallas Morning News,* 2000. http://alamo-de-parras.welkin/org/archives/newsarch/eyebrows.html (2/20/03)

Biffle, Kent. "Through a Lens, Starkly." *The Dallas Morning News.* Oct. 11, 2003.

Chapman, Art. "Alamo Film Scene May Rile Many." *Star-Telegram.* Dec. 4, 2002.

Cieply, Michael and Eller, Claudia. "Film Remembers the Alamo, Inclusively." *Los Angeles Times.* March 1, 2003.

Davis, Bill. "Props that Eat: An Account of a Background Extra (Part 2)." *http://www.thealamofilm.com/billz.htm,* Oct. 7, 2003.

Garcia, Chris. "I Don't Want My Parents to Have to Leave the State." *Austin American Statesmen.* Oct. 11, 2002.

Groneman, Bill. *Death of a Legend.* Plano, Texas: Republic of Texas Press, 1999.

Groneman, Bill. *Defense of a Legend.* Plano, Texas: Wordware Publishing, Inc., 1994.

Huddleston, Scott. "Then and Now-Historic Ozzy-Rocker has Storied Past in S.A. He Urinated on a Monument in 1982." *San Antonio Express-News*, Feb. 16, 2003. p. 2B

Hutton, Paul Andrew. *A Narrative Life of David Crockett.* Lincoln and London: University of Nebraska Press, 1987.

Leydon, Joe. "Revising the Alamo." *http://www.nydailynews.com/front/story/109629p-99048c.html*, Sep. 25, 2003.

Lyman, Rick. "Mexican's Memoir of Alamo a Rage: Story of Davy Crockett's Execution is going on Auction Block." *New York Times*, Nov. 18, 1998. p. A20

Rosenthal and Groneman. *Roll Call at the Alamo.* Ft. Collins, Colorado, 1985. p. 29-37

Shlachter, Barry. "Doubts Remain about Authenticity of Account of Battle of the Alamo." *Fort Worth Star-Telegram.* November 18, 1998.

Stax Report. Script Review of *The Alamo.* [Online] *http://filmforce.ign.com/articles/365/365074p1.html*, July 18, 2002.

Tinkle, Lon. *The Alamo, or 13 Days of Glory.* New York: Published as a Signet Book by arrangement with McGraw-Hill Book Company, September 1960. p. 138-139

Wloszczyna, Susan. "Billy Bob is Davy in Differently Remembered 'Alamo'." *USA Today*. March 6, 2003.

www.thealamofilm.com/faq.htm What styles, viewpoints, and themes will be emphasized? What is the release date? Feb. 20, 2003.

Chapter 4

Adams, Michael C.C. (1990). *The Great Adventure*. Indiana University Press, Indianapolis: p. 7

Bowden, Mark (1999). *Black Hawk Down: A Story of Modern War*. Atlantic Monthly Press: New York.

Brantley, James (Jan., 1993). "Dereliction of Duty". *Soldier of Fortune*. p.30-35, 71

CNN.Com. "Book: Jessica Lynch Was Raped." http://www.cnn.com/2003/US/11/06/lynch.book.ap/. November 6, 2003.

Fehrenbach, T.R. (1963). *This Kind of War*. Pocket Books, Inc., New York: p. 706

Gutmann, Stephanie (2000). *The Kinder, Gentler Military*. Scribner: New York

Holy Bible, The King James Version, I Peter Ch 3, V7

Mitchell, Brian (1989). *Weak Link, The Feminization of the American Military.* Regnery Gateway: Washington, D.C.

Sasser, First Sergeant Charles W. (March, 1992). "Women in Combat, One Grunt's Opinion." *Soldier of Fortune*: p. 38-41, 74

Shakespeare, William (1948). Edited by G.B. Harrison. *Shakespeare, The Complete Works.* Harcourt, Brace and World, Inc. New York: p. 353, 364, 1193, 1195

Women in Combat, Report to the President: Presidential Commission on the Assignment of Women in the Armed Forces (1993). Brassey's: New York

Vistica, Gregory L. (Feb. 5, 1996). "Anchors Aweigh." *Newsweek*: p. 69-71

Chapter 5

Limbaugh, Rush. "My Conversation with Bjorn Lomborg." *The Limbaugh Letter*, May 2002: p. 6-10

Lomborg, Bjorn. *The Skeptical Environmentalist.* Cambridge: Cambridge University Press, 2001.

Moore, Patrick. "Environmentalism For the Twenty-First Century." *You Are Being Lied To.* New York: The Disinformation Company, 2001. p. 296-303

Ridley, Matt. "The Borking of Bjorn Lomborg." *The American Spectator*, March/April 2002: p. 52-53

Chapter 6

Colodny, Robert. *Paradigms and Paradoxes-The Philosophical Challenge of the Quantum Domain.* Pittsburgh: University of Pittsburgh Press, 1972.

Folger, Tim. "Does the Universe Exist if We're Not Looking?" *Discover*, June, 2002. p. 44-8

Karlgaard, Rich. "Incomparable Carver." *Forbes*, March 18, 2002. p. 39

Mead, Carver. "Carver Mead The Spectator Interview." *The American Spectator.* September/October, 2001. p. 68-75

Mead, Carver. *Collective Electrodynamics.* Cambridge, Massachusetts: The MIT Press, 2001.

Sachs, Mendel. *Einstein Versus Bohr.* La Salle, Illinois: Open Court, 1988.

Whitaker, Andrew. *Einstein, Bohr and the Quantum Dilemma.* New York: Cambridge University Press, 1996.

Chapter 7

Brass, Michael. "Tracing Graham Hancock's Shifting Cataclysm." *Skeptical Inquirer*, July/August 2002. p. 45-49

Hancock, Graham. *Fingerprints of the Gods.* New York: Three Rivers Press, 1995.

Schoch, Robert. *Voices Of The Rocks.* New York: Harmony Books, 1999.

West, John Anthony. *Serpent In The Sky.* New York: Harper and Row, 1979.

Chapter 8

Behe, Michael J. *Darwin's Black Box.* New York: Simon and Schuster, 1996.

Crichton, Michael. *The Lost World.* New York: Random House, 1995.

Gore, Rick. "The First Pioneer? A New Find Shakes the Human Family Tree." *National Geographic*, August 2002, Vol. 202 No. 2.

Gould, Stephen J.(1977). *Natural History* 86, 14.

Hanegraaff, Hank. *The Farce of Evolution.* Nashville: Word Publishing, 1998.

Hawking, Stephen. *A Brief History of Time.* New York: Bantam Books, 1998.

Johnson, Phillip E. "The Church of Darwin", *The Wall Street Journal.* August 16, 1999.

Klesius, Michael. "The Big Bloom: How Flowering Plants Changed the World", *National Geographic,* July, 2002. p. 102-121

Perloff, James. *Tornado in a Junkyard.* Massachusetts: Refuge Books, 1999.

Wells, Jonathan. *Icons of Evolution.* Washington, D.C.: Regnery Publishing, 2000.

Wells, Jonathan. "Survival of the Fakest", *The American Spectator.* December 2000/January 2001. p. 19-27

Chapter 9

Chatters, James. *Ancient Encounters-Kennewick Man and the First Americans.* New York: Simon and Schuster, 2001.

Downey, Roger. *Riddle of the Bones-Politics, Science, Race, and the Story of Kennewick Man.* New York: Copernicus, 2000.

Hancock, Graham. *Fingerprints of the Gods.* New York: Three Rivers Press, 1995.

Hayden, Thomas. "Old Bones-Pioneer Stock." *U.S. News & World Report,* Dec. 16, 2002. p.58

Miller, John J. "Remains of the Day - Politics Buries a Key Archeological Find." *National Review*, March 8, 1999.

Thomas, David. *Skull Wars-Kennewick Man, Archeology, and the Battle for Native American Identity.* New York: Basic Books, 2000.

Chapter 10

Creasy, Edward S. *The Fifteen Decisive Battles of the World: From Marathon to Waterloo.* New York, 1908.

Delbruck, Hans. *The Barbarian Invasions, vol. 2 of the History of the Art of War.* Westport, Connecticut, 1980.

Eggenberger, David. *An Encyclopedia of Battles: Accounts of Over 1,560 Battles from 1479 B.C. to the Present.* New York: Dover Publications, Inc., 1985.

Hanson, Victor Davis. *Carnage and Culture: Landmark Battles In The Rise of Western Power.* New York: Doubleday Books, 2001.

Reston Jr., James. *Warriors of God: Richard the Lionhearted and Saladin in the Third Crusade.* C-Span II Book TV Lecture. Aug. 25, 2001.

Book Order Form

- ❑ Yes, please rush me _____ copy/copies of *Suppressed History: Obliterating Politically Correct Orthodoxies*

Name: ________________
Address: ________________
City: ______________ State:______
Zipcode: ____________

When ordering *Suppressed History*, send a check or money order for $19.95 (Free First Class Shipping) to Armistead Publishing, P.O. Box 54516, Cincinnati, OH 45254, or pay by credit card.

Visa or MasterCard Number:

____

Expiration Date:

____